IT'S NEVER TOO LATE

1ST EDITION

Written by

James Pattinson, Julia Cockerham, Latreya Nelson and Eddy Nicholls

Illustrations by

Julia Cockerham, Alex Copeman, Eddy Nicholls and Yabaewah Scott
Cover art: Alex Copeman

Lettering by

HdE

[Re]Start: It's Never Too Late is a work of fiction. Names, characters, places and incidents are the products of the author's imagination or are used fictitiously. Any resemblance to actual events, locales, or persons, living or dead is entirely coincidental.

Published by arrangement with Whitefox Publishing, 25 Horsell Rd, London N5 1XL.

First published in the UK 2023 by The Strategy Shop, London. www.thestrategy.shop

A CIP record is available from the British Library and Bodleian Library.

ISBN 978-1-915036-36-0

Printed in the UK.

IMAGINE GROWING IN MORE WAYS THAN YOU THOUGHT POSSIBLE.
THIS WILL HELP YOU FIGURE OUT WHERE YOU WANT TO GO...
...WHERE YOU'RE AT NOW...
...AND HOW TO GET TO WHERE YOU WANT TO BE.
IT'S BEEN WRITTEN BY PEOPLE FROM A VARIETY OF BACK-GROUNDS.
PEOPLE WHO'VE BEEN THERE AND DONE THAT, TOGETHER WITH PEOPLE WHO ARE STILL FIGURING IT OUT.
IT'S PACKED FULL OF SUGGESTIONS. SOME OF IT WILL WORK FOR YOU AND SOME WON'T. WE'RE ALL DIFFERENT. TAKE WHAT YOU NEED.
#1 MUM

WORLD-CLASS INSIGHT AND TOOLS. MADE REAL.
THIS BOOK IS AN INTERACTIVE PERSONAL GUIDE, SO DRAW AND WRITE ON IT.
08
CREDSTART
THERE'S PLENTY OF SPACE TO MAKE IT YOUR OWN.
CREDSTART
ATS
06 POP UP DO
05 KC
04 JETTS
03 FLEX
02 JAJUTR
01 POP

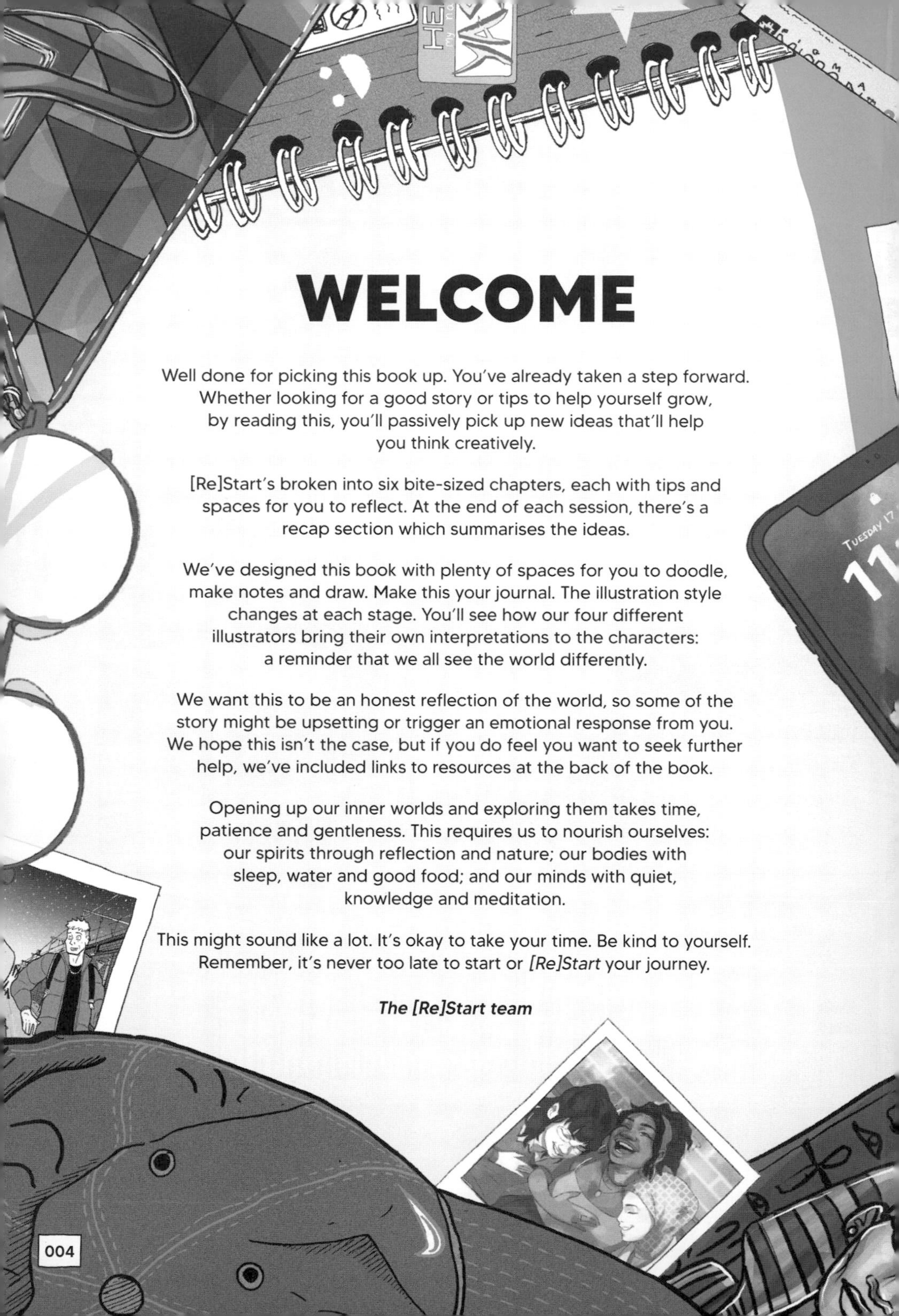

WELCOME

Well done for picking this book up. You've already taken a step forward. Whether looking for a good story or tips to help yourself grow, by reading this, you'll passively pick up new ideas that'll help you think creatively.

[Re]Start's broken into six bite-sized chapters, each with tips and spaces for you to reflect. At the end of each session, there's a recap section which summarises the ideas.

We've designed this book with plenty of spaces for you to doodle, make notes and draw. Make this your journal. The illustration style changes at each stage. You'll see how our four different illustrators bring their own interpretations to the characters: a reminder that we all see the world differently.

We want this to be an honest reflection of the world, so some of the story might be upsetting or trigger an emotional response from you. We hope this isn't the case, but if you do feel you want to seek further help, we've included links to resources at the back of the book.

Opening up our inner worlds and exploring them takes time, patience and gentleness. This requires us to nourish ourselves: our spirits through reflection and nature; our bodies with sleep, water and good food; and our minds with quiet, knowledge and meditation.

This might sound like a lot. It's okay to take your time. Be kind to yourself. Remember, it's never too late to start or *[Re]Start* your journey.

The [Re]Start team

CONTENTS

LET'S GO.

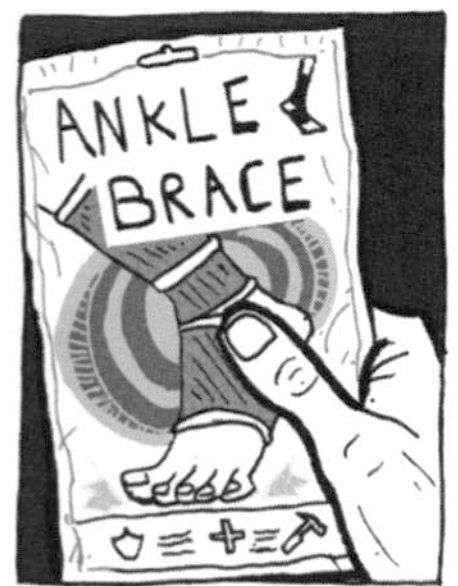
ANKLE BRACE

CLICK
OI, WHERE YOU GOING?

PROLOGUE

EVERYONE FACES DIFFERENT CHALLENGES

DO US A FAVOUR AND DON'T HURRY BACK, EH?
GIVE ME AND YOUR MUM SOME MORE ALONE TIME!
Sigh...
HERE, FAM.
LOVE, BRO.
YO TJ, YOU WANNA GO TO THE TUNNEL LATER? AJ TRACEY'S PLAYING.
THE TUNNEL
BRUV, SHE WAS LENG! YOU GET HER NUMBER?
HAHA, NAH, MAN. YOU KNOW ME...
...I'VE ONLY GOT EYES FOR YOU BAZ!
YO TEEJ.
BRO, ALLOW IT!
WHEN YOU COMING BACK TO TRACK? THE TEAM'S MISSING OUR MAIN GUY! IT'S NEARLY BEEN A WHOLE YEAR!
I, UM...

WEOR
POLICE
CAR WASH
OI!
RUN!
NEE NOR NEE NOR
BZZZ
BZZZ
BZZZ
BZZZ
SHIT!
FUCK'S SAKE...
...NOT AGAIN...
TESCO
TJ. YOU'RE LATE.
I KNOW, I'M SO SORRY.

I HAD SOME ISSUES TO DEAL WITH LAST NIGHT AND THEN MY ANKLE FLARED UP AGAIN.
I'D HAVE MADE IT IF I DIDN'T HAVE TO LIMP ALL THE--

I'M SORRY, TJ, BUT I'M GOING TO HAVE TO LET YOU GO. THIS ISN'T THE FIRST, OR EVEN SECOND TIME THIS HAS HAPPENED. IT'S PUTTING PRESSURE ON THE TEAM.
YOU CAN RETURN YOUR UNIFORM TO THE OFFICE.
SO WHY'D YOU GO OUT WITH THE GUYS AGAIN? YOU KNOW IT ALWAYS ENDS IN TROUBLE.
THEY'RE MY BOYS, GEORGIE!
WOW, I'M SO SORRY. I NOW SEE YOU HAD NO CHOICE IN THE MATTER.
TJ, C'MON, WE'RE MORE LIKE SIBLINGS THAN COUSINS. I KNOW YOU CAN COME UP WITH A BETTER EXCUSE THAN THAT.
WELL, KYE WAS THERE TOO.
YOU KNOW HE'S A DECENT GUY. THAT'S ***PROOF*** WE DIDN'T DO ANYTHING WRONG!
HE WAS? KYE'S THE ONE FROM TRACK, RIGHT?
WHEN ARE YOU GONNA JOIN BACK AGAIN?
OR HAVE YOU STILL NOT GOT A DATE FOR YOUR ANKLE OPERATION?
CAFE
CLOS

I REALLY DON'T WANNA TALK ABOUT THAT RIGHT NOW...

OK, WELL, HOW'S AUNTIE ABBIE DOING? MY MUM MENTIONED SHE DIDN'T SHOW AT HER BIRTHDAY DRINKS THE OTHER WEEK?
SHE HAD WORK... BUT YEAH, SHE'S...

...SHE'S STILL WITH THAT WASTEMAN BARRY.

Nom

Sip

I'M SORRY.

SO WHAT'S UP WITH YOU, G?
OH YEAH! I WAS GONNA SAY I ACTUALLY JUST FINISHED THIS BUSINESS COURSE THING! I THINK YOU SHOULD TAKE A LOOK--
URM, HEY GEORGIE...

...ARE YOU OK TO GET THIS ONE?
AGAIN! TJ! THIS WAS MEANT TO BE YOUR TURN!
PLEASE, G. I PROMISE I'LL PAY YOU BACK ASAP. I'M JUST WAITING FOR MY LAST PAY CHEQUE TO COME THROUGH.

FINE. BUT YOU'VE GOT TO CHECK OUT THIS COURSE.

HI ALL.
MUM!
HEY MUM.
PETE, CAN YOU GET DINNER READY FOR LUKE AND ISAAC? I'M ONLY POPPING BACK TO CHANGE. THEY NEED ME BACK AT WORK.
MUM, I'M KINDA BUSY.
I'VE GOT SO MUCH TO DO AND I'M ALREADY TAKING THEM TO SCHOOL TOMORROW.
SORRY, HONEY, BUT I *HAVE* TO GO TO WORK. ANYWAY I WASN'T ASKING, SO UP YOU GET.
I'M LITERALLY TRYING TO APPLY FOR JOBS RIGHT NOW--
PETER.
OK! SORRY, YES, FINE. I'LL DO IT.
ST JAMES SCHOOL
ST JAMES

UH... **HEY!** SORRY, EXCUSE ME! SIR! **SIR!**
HEY! SORRY, YOU DROPPED THIS.

WOAH, THANKS! GONNA NEED THAT.
YOU WORK AT GOOBLE, HUH? THAT'S AWESOME. YOU MUST GET ALL KINDS OF NEW TECH.
YEAH? DON'T KNOW ABOUT "AWESOME," BUT I CERTAINLY ENJOY IT. YOU INTO TECH, THEN?
YEAH, MASSIVELY. ACTUALLY...

...I NEARLY DID THIS COOL SCHOLAR-SHIP AT MIT IN AMERICA.
NICE, WELL YOU CAN ALWAYS TRY AND GET IN ANOTHER TIME.
OH, I MEAN I GOT THE SCHOLAR-SHIP... IT'S JUST, THEN MY DAD GOT SICK AND COVID HAPPENED...
awkward scratch
THAT'S NOT EASY, KID.
TELL YOU WHAT. I WAS TALKING TO AN INTERN RECENTLY WHO HAD A SIMILAR SITUATION. HE SAID THIS COURSE IN HACKNEY REALLY HELPED HIM.
MIGHT BE WORTH CHECKING IT OUT.
IT'S A BIT MORE LOCAL THAN AMERICA, TOO... GOOD LUCK!

Hip Hop Mix
By Spookify
PLAYLIST

Marshall
EST 1962

SOPHIE, DARLING!
LUNCH IS READY!

STORES
JOBS
SALES ASSISTANT
Working within a small and friendl retail team where everyone looks out for each other, team rk
FLOOR MANAGER

SOPHIE, DO YOU HAVE TO LISTEN TO THAT MUSIC SO LOUDLY? I'M SURE THE NEIGHBOURS CAN HEAR YOU.
Yuval Harari
apiens
A Brief History of Humankind

ESPECIALLY WHEN YOU LEAVE YOUR WINDOWS OPEN, AS YOU ***ALWAYS*** DO...

WHAT'VE YOU BEEN UP TO THIS MORNING, DARLING? ANYTHING PRODUCTIVE?
I WAS ACTUALLY LOOKING AT THIS PART TIME JOB OPENING AT THIS CLOTHING SHOP IN EASTFIELD.
THEIR STUFF IS ***SOOO*** PENG. I MIGHT APPLY.

IF YOU'RE INTERESTED IN RETAIL, THERE'S NO NEED FOR PART-TIME GRUNT WORK. YOU SHOULD CHAT TO THE BARRINGTONS WHEN YOU SEE THEM THIS EVENING.
I'M SURE THEY COULD ARRANGE SOMETHING MORE FITTING FOR YOU IN ONE OF THEIR STORES.
Yuval Harari
apiens
A Brief History of Humankind

THE BARRINGTONS?
OH YES, YOUR FATHER AND I HAVE ARRANGED FOR YOU TO GO TO THE BARRINGTON-SMYTH'S FOR EMMA'S BIRTHDAY PARTY THIS EVENING.
BUT MUM! MY FRIENDS AREN'T EVEN GOING, AND YOU KNOW I HATE THOSE THINGS!
THEY'RE SO DRY AND THE BARRINGTON'S ARE SO... UGH.
WELL, YOUR FATHER AND I ARE OTHERWISE ENGAGED, YOUR SISTER HAS GOT HER PIANO RECITAL AND IT WOULD BE GOOD FOR OUR FAMILY TO BE REPRESENTED.
AFTER ALL, YOUR FATHER AND I HAVE ALREADY SAID YOU WOULD GO.
WHAT MUSIC DO YOU LIKE?
I'VE RECENTLY BEEN ENJOYING THE CLASSICS ACTUALLY...
...THE ROLLING STONES, MEATLOAF...
AND YOU, SOPHIE?
OH, I JUST LISTEN TO ANYTHING, REALLY...
I THOUGHT BEA TOLD ME YOU WERE INTO RAP?
WELL, I CERTAINLY WOULDN'T HAVE GUESSED THAT!
I CAN NEVER TELL WHAT THEY'RE SAYING...

WE'RE GOING SHOOTING TOMORROW.
GILLERS AND TOMMO ARE COMING. AND ANNABELLE.
FANCY TAGGING ALONG, SOPHIE?
ERM, SORRY I'M BUSY TOMORROW...
YOUR LOSS.
TAXI
UHH, LETS SEE... PICK UP FOR SOPHIE?
OH... ARE YOU OKAY?
YEAH. I'M FINE.
I'M AFRAID I'VE GOT THREE DAUGHTERS, SO YOU CAN'T FOOL ME.
WHAT'S GOT YOU DOWN, HUH?
REALLY. I'M FINE.
I... I JUST DON'T FEEL RIGHT... LIKE THINGS DON'T MAKE SENSE FOR ME THE WAY THEY SEEM TO FOR EVERYONE ELSE, LIKE MY FRIENDS AND FAMILY. I'M JUST SO CONFUSED...
...Sorry.

IT'S OK. IT'S NORMAL TO FEEL THAT WAY.
LIFE CAN BE VERY CONFUSING AND YOU'RE ONLY YOUNG.
I GUESS...
YOU KNOW, I WAS AN ENGINEER IN IRAN BUT NOW I DRIVE TO LOOK AFTER MY FAMILY. LIFE IS A FUNNY GAME.
WOW, THAT MUST HAVE BEEN HARD.
SURE. IT WAS TOUGH.
HE LEFT SOME FLYERS IN THE BACK SEAT POCKET FOR MY DAUGHTERS.
PLEASE TAKE ONE.
[RE] START YOUR
I HAD TO MAKE SACRIFICES, BUT MY FAMILY IS SAFER HERE.
ONLY...
IT'S A DIFFERENT WORLD NOW.
YOU KNOW, MY OTHER PASSENGER WAS A VERY GOOD BUSINESSMAN. HE SAID HE RUNS A COURSE THAT MAKES SENSE OF THE WORLD FOR YOUNG PEOPLE LIKE YOU.
AND IF YOU GO, TELL THEM HADI FROM THE TAXI SENT YOU!

WHERE ARE YOU OFF TO, JAIDEEP?*
*TRANSLATED FROM PUNJABI.
TUTANKHAMUN
JUST OUT WITH SOME MATES.
OK, BUT DON'T FORGET DINNER THIS EVENING.
SEE YOU SOON, PUTTAR.
SURE.
THE DAILY
...
WHAT DO YOU THINK YOU'RE DOING, YOUNG LADY?
MA, COULD I POSSIBLY MAYBE GO TO THIS EXHIBITION AT THE MUSEUM WITH EMILY?
TUTANKHAMUN
NOT TODAY. WHY DON'T YOU STAY AND HELP PREPARE DINNER? YOUR MASI'S COMING OVER. WE'VE A LOT TO GET READY.
FINE...

SO, PRIYA, WHAT ARE YOU UP TO AT THE MOMENT? HOW ARE THE A-LEVELS GOING?
PRETTY GOOD. I WAS THINKING I MIGHT STUDY CLASSICS AT UNI.
WHAT?! NO.
I THINK YOU SHOULD STUDY BUSINESS. WHAT WILL CLASSICS GET YOU?

THAT'S NOT REALLY THE POINT, PAPA...
OH DON'T BE SILLY. JUST LOOK AT YOUR CHACHA.
YOU'LL HAVE PLENTY OF TIME FOR YOUR HISTORY HOBBY ONCE YOU'VE GOT A GOOD JOB, NICE HOUSE AND LOVING HUSBAND.

SQUEK
PSHHHH

SO YOU'RE INTERESTED IN HISTORY, BETA?
NOT THAT IT MATTERS, APPARENTLY...

WELL, NOW YOU ARE BEING SILLY. DID YOU KNOW I'M TAKING A NIGHT CLASS TO IMPROVE MY ENGLISH AT THE MOMENT?

AHA, NO.
GUESS NOT.

OH YEAH?

MMHM. AND DO YOU THINK YOUR CHACHA *APPROVES* OF THAT?

LOOK, PRIYA. DO ME A FAVOUR.
THERE'S SOMETHING I WANT YOU TO CHECK OUT. IT'S A NEW PROGRAMME I FOUND OUT ABOUT FROM ONE OF THE LADIES AT WORK...

TAK
TAK
TAK
YASMIN! MENDEKA!
ZA KAWA!
URGH, THE BUS IS FULL OF PEOPLE LIKE HER THESE DAYS.
HALF OF THEM DON'T EVEN SPEAK ENGLISH.

BABA, I CAN'T WAIT TILL YOU RESTART YOUR JOB AS A SURGEON SOON.*
*TRANSLATED FROM PASHTO.

LOOK YASMIN, DON'T WORRY ABOUT ME. YOUR MOR AND I JUST WANT YOU AND YOUR BROTHER TO HAVE THE BEST OPPORTUNITIES IN LIFE.

RIIINNGG
ORCHARD SCHOOL

ART
YASMIN! WAIT A MOMENT!

YOU'VE GOT A REAL CREATIVE GIFT, YASMIN, HAVE YOU EVER THOUGHT ABOUT PURSUING IT SERIOUSLY?

I ENJOY IT. IT'S JUST... IS ART EVEN A JOB?

OF COURSE IT IS!
LOOK, IT'S GOING TO BE TIME TO APPLY FOR UNIVERSITY SOON.
I KNOW YOU'VE BEEN LOOKING AT PURSUING YOUR SKILLS IN MATHS, BUT I'D LOVE TO SEE YOU CONSIDER SOME ART SCHOOLS AS WELL.

I DON'T KNOW, I FEEL LIKE MY PARENTS WOULD PREFER ME TO GO MORE ACADEMIC, IT JUST FEELS MORE PRACTICAL OR...
...AMBITIOUS.

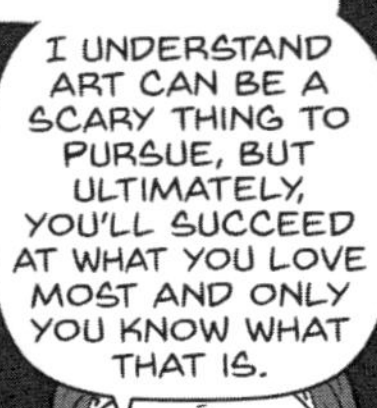
I UNDERSTAND ART CAN BE A SCARY THING TO PURSUE, BUT ULTIMATELY, YOU'LL SUCCEED AT WHAT YOU LOVE MOST AND ONLY YOU KNOW WHAT THAT IS.

IF YOU'RE UNSURE, PERHAPS I COULD RECOMMEND SOME-THING THAT MIGHT HELP YOU MAKE UP YOUR MIND?

HONG KONG

...AND SO, STUDYING IN LONDON IS A WONDERFUL CHANCE TO IMPROVE YOUR ENGLISH SKILLS...*
*TRANSLATED FROM CANTONESE.

...ENGAGE IN A NEW CULTURE...

...AND GROW YOUR CONFIDENCE.

COULD YOU IMAGINE? I'D BE TERRIFIED!
記得
I KNOW. THOUGH I THINK I COULD MANAGE.
BUT I WOULDN'T WANT TO LEAVE MY FRIENDS. ESPECIALLY YOU, XIAOFENG!
WHAT ABOUT YOU, ANDI?

I--

ARE YOU KIDDING? ANDI'S SO SHY!
DO YOU NOT REMEMBER HOW LONG IT TOOK HER TO MAKE FRIENDS WITH US?
緊急

stand up comedy

...GROW YOUR CONFIDENCE...
...ARE YOU KIDDING? ANDI'S SO SHY!
LONDON IS A WONDERFUL CHANCE...
SLAM
YOU MAKE SURE TO CALL US AS SOON AS YOU LAND!
AND REMEMBER TO ENJOY IT!
Terminal 2
T2
WE'RE SO PROUD OF YOU, DEAR.
THANKS, MAMA. THANKS BABA. LOVE YOU BOTH LOTS.
STUDY ABROAD BUCKET LIST.
o Go to Comedy nights
Find my "people"
o Get involved in Communities.
o Improve english.
o Improve confidence!

"NOW I'D LIKE YOU ALL TO MEET OUR NEW STUDENT."
THIS IS ANDI. SHE'S TRAVELLED ALL THE WAY FROM HONG KONG. CARE TO TELL US A BIT ABOUT YOURSELF?
H-HELLO EVERYONE. I AM, UH - ANDI AND... AND I - I HAVE LIVED MOST OF MY LIFE IN BEIJING BEFORE MOVING TO HONG KONG.
SO, UM, I AM THOROUGHLY EX-EXCITED TO EXPERIENCE YOUR CITY AND, UH, CULTURE.
THANK YOU, ANDI. SO TODAY...
Chatter Chatter Chatter
HEYA! I'M MIA. JUST A HEADS UP: THOROUGHLY IS PRONOUNCED "THURR-UH-LEE."
Chatter Chuckle Chatter
WHAT ARE YOU DOING HERE?
YOU CAN BARELY EVEN MAKE FRIENDS IN YOUR OWN LANGUAGE.
IDIOT.
HOW ARE YOU SETTLING IN? HAVE YOU MADE ANY FRIENDS YET?*
NOT YET... I'VE ONLY BEEN HERE A COUPLE OF DAYS.
WELL HOW ABOUT JOINING ANY CLUBS? THAT COULD BE A GOOD WAY TO MEET SOME PEOPLE!
I WILL, BUT I DON'T KNOW... I'M JUST GETTING SETTLED. IT'S ALL SO DIFFERENT.
YEAR PLAN
*TRANSLATED FROM CANTONESE.

OK, ANDI. REMEMBER, IF THINGS ARE TOO MUCH, COMING HOME IS ALWAYS AN OPTION.

THANKS MAMA. BUT THAT'S OK. I'M FINE. I WANT TO STAY.

BESIDES, I REALLY DON'T WANT TO FAIL THIS TERM.

BZZ BZZ

Baba
Have you joined a club yet? Choose one that looks fun!

Sigh...

community board

OK, ANDI... WHERE ARE YOUR PEOPLE?

FLYERS – Please take!

THE GREEN SOC!

comedy club.

GOT JUNK?

BOOK CLUB

EARTH DAY

SHIT!

CHatter CHatter CHatter

51B

RANDOM GRAB

IT'S THOSE GIRLS!

AFTERNOON, PRINCESA!
HOW ARE YOU DOING?
I'M OK, MOM. GOING OUT TO THIS THING WITH SOME FRIENDS.
HAVE FUN. BE SAFE. AND IF YOU CAN'T BE SAFE, BE CAREFUL!

YEAH, THE BAND'S GOING GREAT.
WE'RE RECORDING NEW MATERIAL AND THE SINGLE'S GETTING SOME DECENT PLAYS.
YIKES, AND HERE I AM WORKING FOR MY DAD. HAHA!

BUT ALAS, 'TIS A HUMBLE LIFE I LEAD, TO CARRY ON THE FAMILY BUSINESS AND ALL. PLUS...

...WHEN NATE WAKES UP FROM HIS DELUSIONS OF BEING A ROCKSTAR...
...I'M SURE MY OLD MAN COULD SORT HIM OUT WITH WORK!

WELL, WHILE YOU LOSERS ARE MIDDLE-AGED STILL WORKING FOR CALLUM'S DAD...
...I'LL BE MAKING BANK AS A PSYCHOLOGIST.

WHAT'RE YOU GOING TO DO AFTER YOUR GAP YEAR, TASH?
YOU'VE NEVER REALLY SAID?

UH, TO BE TOTALLY HONEST, I HAVEN'T REALLY GOT ANY PLANS. MY MOMS ARE SUPER CHILLED.
THEY JUST WANT ME TO BE HAPPY OR WHATEVER...
SO IT'S DECIDED.
TASH WILL BE NEEDING A JOB FROM MY DAD TOO! I WARN YOU THOUGH, AFTER HE MEETS THIS WASTEMAN...
...IT COULD BE A WHILE BEFORE HE HIRES ANOTHER ONE OF MY MATES!
AHahHaHa HAahHah haHAhaH
SERIOUSLY THOUGH, YOU'VE NO IDEA WHAT YOU'RE GOING TO DO? ARE YOU JUST GOING TO STAY IN RETAIL FOREVER?
OR, LIKE, GO BACK TO AMERICA?
06

00:48
tashpanda
704 posts
55k follows
870 following
Tash she/her
personal blog
edit profile
website
insights
ads
fits
paris
home
luvs

boost
view insights
liked by juliaca and 1,572 others
drinks up <3

00:50
Instagram

1m 1 like Reply
lolatoast SO radient!
1m 1 like Reply
antedward Sheesh...
2m 1 like Reply
beautbods prettyface
2m 1 like Reply
itsagracie stunning
5m 1 like Reply
I'm in love.

00:56
[Re]Start
Sponsored
Feeling lost?

Learn More
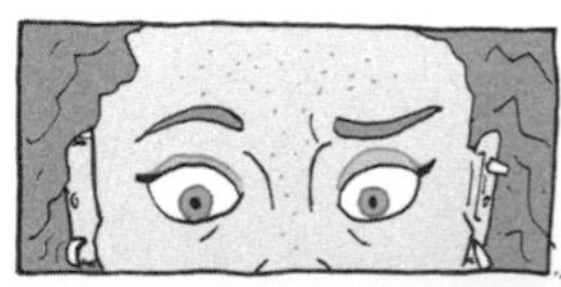
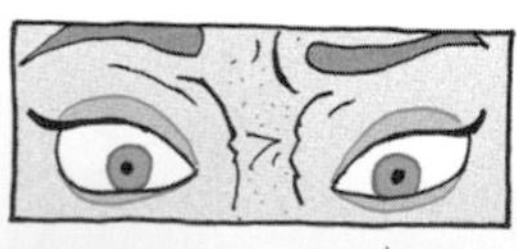

[RE]STAR
NOW!
Discover and get to your dreams.
london based
Learn More

SKIP

00:57
clare_wj 1h
GUESS WHO GOT ON TO THEIR DREAM UNI COURSE...
Send message

00:57
natemusicmate 2h
NEW SINGLE!!
OUT NOW!!
LINK IN BIO!!
Send message
SCREW IT...
Gooble
[RE]START LONDON
Gooble Search
I'm feeling lucky

STAGE ZERO

[RE]START ASSEMBLE

"IF YOU DON'T LIKE SOMETHING, CHANGE IT. IF YOU CAN'T CHANGE IT, CHANGE YOUR ATTITUDE."

MAYA ANGELOU*

*MAYA ANGELOU WAS AN AMERICAN MEMOIRIST, POPULAR POET AND CIVIL RIGHTS ACTIVIST.

WELCOME TO [RE]START
BIG
HEY MAN. I'M PETE.
NICE ONE, PETEY BOI! I'M TJ.
SICK PLACE...
SLAP

OH MY GOD, I'M SO NERVOUS.
THIS IS BUILDING HUGE!
I'M TASH BY THE WAY.
I KNOW RIGHT?! I'M PRIYA.
YASMIN. NICE TO MEET YOU.

6 BITE SIZED STEPS

TO REALISING YOUR DREAM

THIS IS *YOUR* JOURNEY

YOU'RE IN CHARGE

PERHAPS THROUGH TALKING WITH OTHER PEOPLE YOU CAN EVEN HELP THEM FIGURE OUT HOW TO GET TO THEIR DREAM.
WHAT DO YOU THINK ABOUT THAT?

WOULD IT HELP TO TALK WITH SOMEONE DIFFERENT FROM US?

USE THE POWER OF DIFFERENCE

DEFINITELY.
EXPLORING HOW DIFFERENT PEOPLE EXPERIENCE THE WORLD IS VITAL. IT BROADENS OUR UNDERSTANDING OF OTHERS AND OURSELVES.

IT MAY BE HARD AT FIRST...

...BUT YOU'LL ACHIEVE GREATER RESULTS TOGETHER, GROWING IN MORE WAYS THAN YOU CAN POSSIBLY IMAGINE.

FIND WAYS THAT WORK BEST FOR YOU

GET IN THE SPACE TO REFLECT *YOUR WAY*

"IT'S IMPORTANT TO FIND WHICH METHODS OF DEEP FOCUS WORK FOR YOU. REFLECTION IS REQUIRED AS YOU GROW. IT'S IMPORTANT TO RECOGNISE THE CHANGES IN YOURSELF.

"FIND TIME TO BE STILL AND SILENT. MUSIC OR AMBIENT NOISE SUCH AS BIRDS OR DISTANT CHATTER IN A CAFÉ MIGHT HELP YOU RELAX AND FOCUS."

CREATE SPACE TO HEAR YOUR INNER VOICE.
BE HONEST WITH YOURSELF ABOUT HOW YOU'RE FEELING.
THERE'S NO POINT FAKING IT TO YOURSELF.

STILLNESS AND SILENCE WILL HELP YOU REFLECT

WHAT DOES REFLECTING MEAN TO YOU?
TRY WRITING DOWN SOME IDEAS ON HOW YOU CAN GET IN THE MOOD, READY TO REFLECT.

THIS SPACE IS FOR YOUR REFLECTIONS | DATE: ....

WHAT GETS YOU IN THE MOOD TO REFLECT?

Remember there's no one way of doing things. Everyone's different. We all think things through in our own way, at our own pace. It's okay to do it your way!

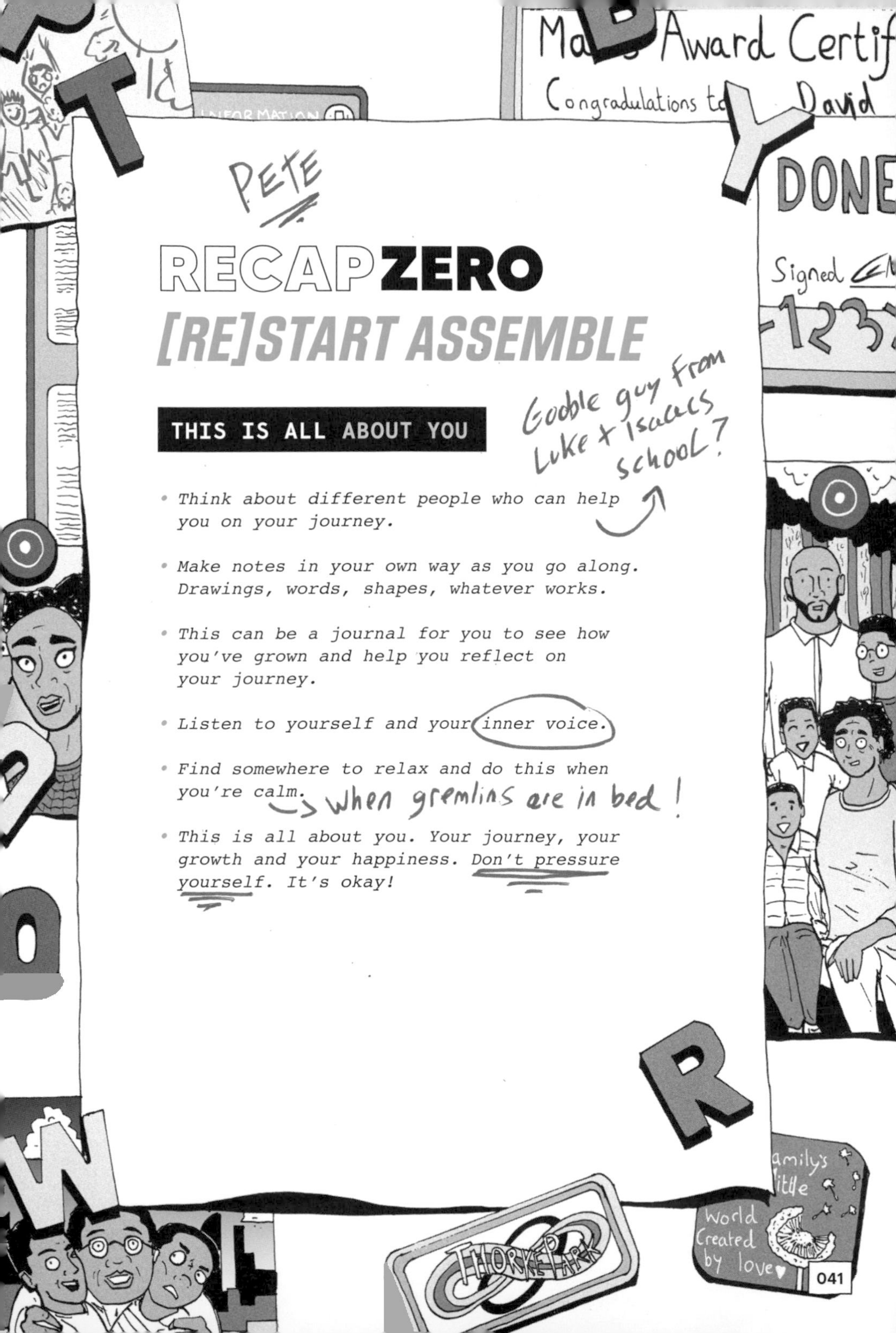

RECAP ZERO

[RE]START ASSEMBLE

THIS IS ALL ABOUT YOU

- *Think about different people who can help you on your journey.*
- *Make notes in your own way as you go along. Drawings, words, shapes, whatever works.*
- *This can be a journal for you to see how you've grown and help you reflect on your journey.*
- *Listen to yourself and your inner voice.*
- *Find somewhere to relax and do this when you're calm.*
- *This is all about you. Your journey, your growth and your happiness. Don't pressure yourself. It's okay!*

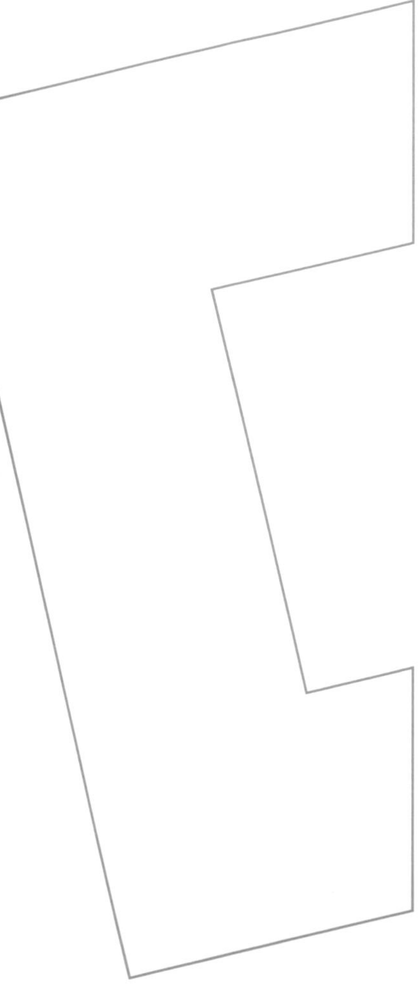

This space has been left for you.

STAGE ONE

IT'S OK

"SORROW LOOKS BACK. WORRY LOOKS AROUND. FAITH LOOKS UP."
RALPH WALDO EMERSON*

*'WALDO' WAS AN AMERICAN ESSAYIST, LECTURER, PHILOSOPHER, ABOLITIONIST AND POET WHO LED THE TRANSCENDENTALIST MOVEMENT OF THE MID-19TH CENTURY.

IT'S OK TO FEEL CONFUSED OR UNSURE.
FEELING NERVOUS IS COMMON FOR PEOPLE NO MATTER YOUR AGE OR WHERE YOU'RE FROM.

DON'T WORRY. REMEMBER, YOU'VE ALREADY GOT THIS FAR.

WHETHER IT'S CLEAR OR UNCLEAR RIGHT NOW, YOU'RE ALREADY HEADING THE RIGHT WAY BECAUSE YOU'VE DECIDED TO (RE)START.

...LIKE, MY PARENTS HAVE SUCH STRONG IDEAS ABOUT WHAT I SHOULD DO AND WHERE I SHOULD GO, **AND** WHO I SHOULD BE WITH...

TELL ME ABOUT IT! MY DAD THINKS I SHOULD STUDY BUSINESS.
IT'S LIKE HE'S ALREADY PLANNED OUT MY **ENTIRE** LIFE REGARDLESS OF WHAT I THINK.

THERE'S THIS QUOTE FROM STORMZY I LOVE... "OUR PARENTS DON'T ALWAYS KNOW WHAT'S RIGHT. IT'S A NEW AGE."

YOOOO, THIS IS MAD, SOPHIE! YOU LISTEN TO STORMZY?!

HEY, WHO DOESN'T LIKE STORMZY?! WHAT'S WRONG WITH SOPHIE LISTENING TO HIM TOO?

WHAT'S MORE, SOPHIE RAISES A WONDERFUL POINT.

IT DOESN'T CHANGE WHEN YOU'RE OLDER, EITHER.
FRIENDS, FAMILY, PARTNERS AND COLLEAGUES ALWAYS HAVE IDEAS ABOUT WHAT YOU SHOULD DO.
ESPECIALLY NOW, THINGS CAN FEEL EXTRA CONFUSING AND UNCERTAIN.

OTHER PEOPLE WILL HAVE OPINIONS

BUT IT'S YOUR LIFE

I FEEL YOU...

"SOME OF MY FRIENDS DON'T THINK LIKE ME. THAT MAKES IT HARD TO DO MY OWN THING AND THERE'S ALWAYS A SHIT-LOAD OF PRESSURE."
I GOTTA STUDY TONIGHT.
COME OUT, BRUV. WHY YOU BEING A WASTEMAN!
YEAH, SERIOUSLY BRO, COME OUT.

REMEMBER THESE ARE *YOUR* CHOICES

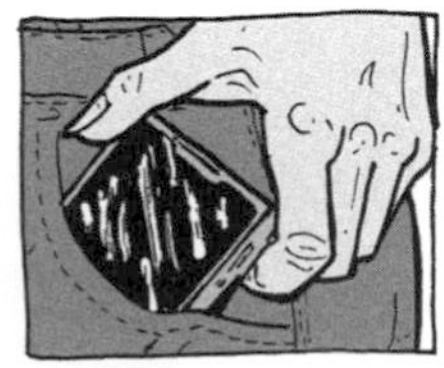

BE PROACTIVE

ALLOW YOURSELF TO FEEL

IT'S OK

THIS SPACE IS FOR YOUR REFLECTIONS | DATE: ....

HOW DO I FEEL? WHY? WRITE DOWN YOUR THOUGHTS

Give yourself the time and space you need to think about your feelings. Writing them down can help you focus.

THIS SPACE IS FOR YOUR REFLECTIONS / DATE: ....

HOW DO I WANT TO FEEL?

Try writing positive feelings you'd like to have.

RECAP ONE

IT'S OK

REFLECT ON HOW YOU FEEL

- It's normal to feel confused or disoriented.
- You're already moving – and you've got this far!
- You're in charge of your own destiny, so you need to make the choices that are right for you.
- Be proactive – take responsibility for your own actions.
- Make things happen, don't wait for them to happen to you.
- Thinking this much is hard work and you'll probably get tired. Change is not easy. It's important to look after yourself with good sleep, good food, water and rest.
- Be kind and gentle to yourself.
- Keep your notes somewhere safe. They'll be useful for you to review later.

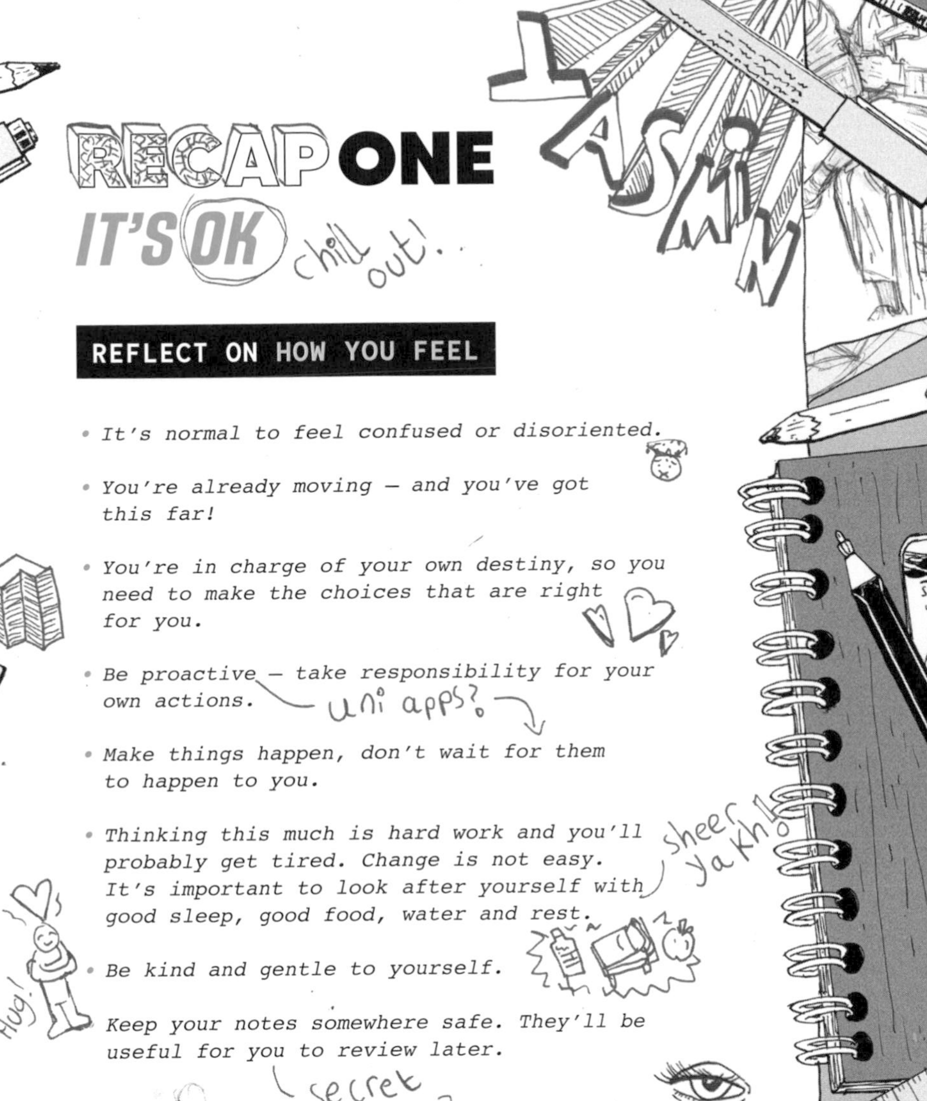

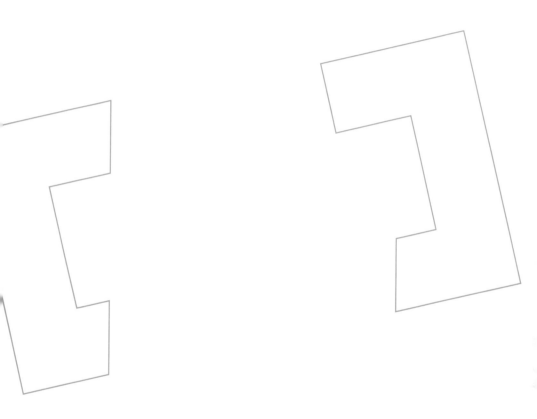

This space has been left for you.

THAT WAS SO INTERESTING! DO YOU GUYS WANT TO GRAB A DRINK? IT'LL BE GREAT TO GET TO KNOW Y'ALL BETTER.
WHAT KIND OF DRINK, TASH?
I KNOW THIS GREAT MILKSHAKE BAR AROUND THE CORNER? I NEED TO GET MY BLOOD SUGAR UP.
YEAH, SURE! SOUNDS CUTE.
NICE! YOU BOYS WANT TO JOIN?
SHRUG
SORRY, I'VE GOT TO GET BACK TO MY BROTHERS.
COPYCAT
YEAH, WE GOTTA GET BACK TO HIS BROTHERS!
SOME OTHER TIME, LADIES...
BOW

...SO YEAH, I DON'T REALLY KNOW WHAT I WANNA DO, LIKE AT ALL...
SO, WHAT BRINGS YOU GUYS HERE?
EWW, GROSS...
I'LL GO.
GO FOR IT, YASMIN!
I GUESS I WANT TO FIGURE OUT WHAT I WANT.
MY PARENTS GAVE UP EVERYTHING IN AFGHANISTAN TO BRING ME HERE.
I WAS HOPING THIS COURSE WOULD HELP ME FIGURE OUT WHAT I WANT TO DO AND SOMEHOW REPAY THEM.
I GET IT. FAMILY IS SO IMPORTANT.
IT'S LIKE EVERY DECISION HAS TO BE MADE SO YOU DON'T LET THEM DOWN.
YEAH! IT'S LIKE TRYING TO WALK ON TWO DIFFERENT TIGHT-ROPES...
...AND THEY'RE GETTING FURTHER AND FURTHER AWAY.
OUCH!
WHAT ABOUT YOU, SOPHIE?

I FEEL THE SAME WITH MY FAMILY, SO AT LEAST YOU'VE GOT ONE FRIEND ON THE SAME PAGE!
I GUESS THE SAME, REALLY. TO FIGURE OUT WHAT I WANT AND SOMEHOW PLEASE MY FAMILY.
I'M NOT SURE IF IT'S ME OR THEM, BUT EVEN WITH MY FRIENDS, IT FEELS LIKE SOMETIMES WE JUST AREN'T ON THE SAME PAGE.
AWH, THANKS, PRIYA!
CLINK
THAT LEAVES YOU... ERM... ANNIE?
IT'S ANDI, ACTUALLY.
!
OH MY GOD, I'M SO SORRY.
IT'S FINE, REALLY.
DAYDREAM
OH!
HOW ABOUT YOU, ANDI?
UMM... I CAME TO LONDON FOR SIXTH FORM. I'M GOING TO START YEAR 12 AND UM, YEAH...
...I GUESS I THOUGHT THE COURSE IS A GOOD THING TO DO FOR UH... ME?
THAT'S REALLY COOL.
BEEP
6.2
Sugar Levels

SO, YOU EVER DONE ONE OF THESE COURSE THINGS BEFORE?
NOPE. NO TIME.
OH. HOW COME?
WELL, MY MUM WORKS A LOT, SO I GOTTA TAKE CARE OF MY LITTLE BROTHERS.
I ACTUALLY FOUND THIS PAID INTERNSHIP RECENTLY...
...AND I'D LOVE TO DO IT. BUT I JUST DON'T HAVE THE TIME FOR IT.
BRUV, GO FOR IT! IT'S PAID! BESIDES, IT'S ONLY GONNA HELP, RIGHT? COULDN'T YOUR DAD COVER FOR YOU?
MY DAD DIED A FEW YEARS AGO...
I'M SO SORRY, FAM... MINE'S NOT AROUND EITHER.
BUT!
JUST TRUST ME, MAN. YOU GOTTA GO FOR IT. THIS COULD BE YOUR CHANCE!
MAYBE...
NAH. NO "MAYBES." PROMISE ME.
OK, FINE. I'LL APPLY.
I'LL UH...
...I'LL CATCH YOU LATER PETEY BOI. IN A BIT, FAM!
"PETEY BOI?"

HA HA HA HA HA HA HA
COME ON REF
OI BARRY. I DIDN'T KNOW YOUR STEPSON KNEW HOW TO READ!
SNATCH
HEY!
ALL RIGHT, CALM DOWN, MATE! IT'S A JOKE.
SNATCH BACK
WHY DON'T YOU LEAVE YOUR LITTLE DIARY AND COME WATCH THE FOOTY WITH US, EH?
BUMP
WHATEVER. SUIT YOURSELF.

IF YOU'RE NOT JOINING, MIND GETTING ME AND THE BOYS A RESTOCK? YOUR MUM'S NOT DOING HER JOB.
AND MAKE SURE IT'S NOT SOME PISS BRAND.
[RE] START

I'LL BE BACK IN A BIT, MUM.

[RE] START

ZZZ
Nat's
ZZZ
I HAD IT FIRST!
GIVE IT!
OW!
IT'S MY TURN!
AND NOW IT'S MY TURN.
SNATCH
WILL YOU TWO SHUT IT?! MUM'S SLEEPING.
IF YOU TWO DON'T STOP, I WILL TAKE THIS REMOTE AND HIDE IT SOMEWHERE YOU'LL NEVER FIND IT.
LIKE UP YOUR BUM!
YOU HAVE THREE SECONDS TO RUN...
GO, GO, GO!
WILL YOU BOYS KEEP IT DOWN? WE HAVE NEIGHBOURS, FOR GOODNESS' SAKE!
PETE STARTED IT!
YOU LITTLE SHIT--
PETER! I WILL NOT HAVE YOU SWEARING IN THIS HOUSE. YOU SHOULD KNOW BETTER.

MOVE.
SHOVE
SHOVE
HEY!
OW...
THOSE LITTLE SHITS--
PETER, I NEED YOU TO FINISH THE BOYS' DINNERS. I'VE BEEN CALLED BACK TO THE HOSPITAL.

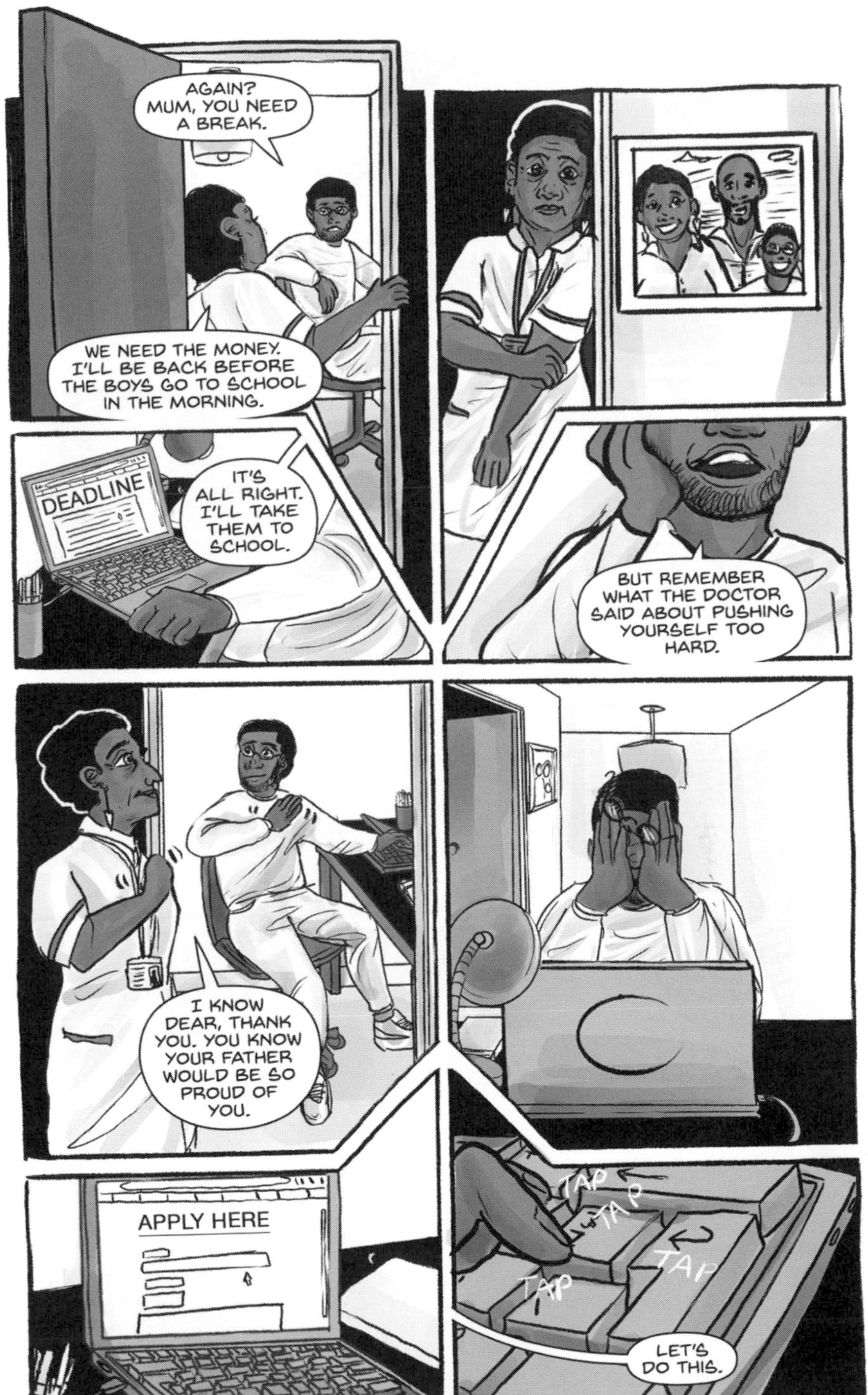
AGAIN? MUM, YOU NEED A BREAK.
WE NEED THE MONEY. I'LL BE BACK BEFORE THE BOYS GO TO SCHOOL IN THE MORNING.
DEADLINE
IT'S ALL RIGHT. I'LL TAKE THEM TO SCHOOL.
BUT REMEMBER WHAT THE DOCTOR SAID ABOUT PUSHING YOURSELF TOO HARD.
I KNOW DEAR, THANK YOU. YOU KNOW YOUR FATHER WOULD BE SO PROUD OF YOU.
APPLY HERE
TAP TAP TAP TAP
LET'S DO THIS.

LATER...
LOOK
STARE
SEE YOU LATER!
TEXT ME!
TAXI
OMG guys, just had the most intense day! You guys should totally check out this course I've joined! x
PING!
PING
PING
PING
OMG guys, just had the most intense day! You guys should totally check out this course I've joined! x
Lol Sophie's joined a cult
Classic Sophie
Send red flag emoji if you need saving!!

Sis
You busy?
What you doing tonight? Want to get a Chinese or something?
I'm busy.

I'M HOME!*
HI, SWEETIE!
*TRANSLATED FROM PUNJABI.

Museum Competition

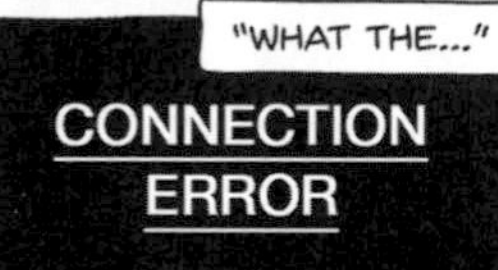
"WHAT THE..."
CONNECTION ERROR

JAIDEEP!
INTERNET'S SLOW. NEED THE CABLE.
I WAS USING IT!

MA! JAIDEEP STOLE THE INTERNET.
DON'T LISTEN TO HER. YOU CAN'T *STEAL* THE INTERNET.
TOO BAD.

PRIYA LET YOUR BROTHER PLAY WITH THE INTERNET. IT'S HIS TURN TO RELAX.
WHAT FOR? HE DOESN'T DO ANYTHING!
WATCH YOUR TONE, YOUNG LADY.
NOW COME HELP ME WITH DINNER.

HA HA
HA
HAHA
HA
HAHA
HA HA
HA
EXCUSE ME.
Masi Pinky
Hope the course went well today! Was thinking of you. X
TAP-TAP TAP
Hope the course went well today! Was thinking of you. X
It went really well thanks! In fact it inspired me to apply for this museum competition, but I got kicked off the computer by Jaideep… x
I'm glad it went well! RE the computer situ: I think your uncle might have a spare laptop lying around. Would you like to borrow it for your competition? x
OMG yes please!! That'd be amazing!! Xx
Great. I'll go ask your uncle where it is. X

*TRANSLATED FROM PASHTO.

SLAM!
HOW WAS THE COURSE?
OH, IT WAS INTERESTING. SOME REALLY USEFUL ADVICE.

YOU MAKE ANY FRIENDS?
MAYBE. IT'S ONLY BEEN ONE SESSION. THOUGH THERE'S A GIRL CALLED TASH WHO SEEMS NICE.

WHAT YOU WATCHING...?

I UM... MUST HAVE FALLEN ASLEEP AND IT TURNED OFF.

GOOD GOOD.

COME ON, SLEEPYHEAD. YOUR MOTHER'S COOKING ENGLISH TONIGHT.
A ROAST DINNER?
NOT SURE REALLY, THERE'S JUST AN AWFUL LOT OF BEIGE ON THE COUNTER!

I'LL BE DOWN IN FIVE...
PUSH

...IT WAS HONESTLY SO EMBARRASSING. I LITERALLY JUST EXPIRED.
O-M-G! MOOD SHIFT. WHOSE IDEA WAS IT TO ADD THIS TO THE PLAYLIST?
IT'S J COLE.
HAHA! OF COURSE YOU'D KNOW IT.
PROD
WHAT'S SO FUNNY? YEAH, I LIKE IT. IT'S A GOOD SONG.
YES, BUT IT DOESN'T EXACTLY SUIT YOUR VIBE, SOPHIE.
CLINK
SLURP
YOU'RE NOT EXACTLY THE URBAN TYPE.
SO ANYWAY, WHAT HAPPENED NEXT, DAN?
OH MY GOD, SO--
URBAN? WHAT DOES THAT EVEN MEAN?

IT'S JUST, LIKE, THE LYRICS ARE LITERALLY TALKING ABOUT EQUALITY IN THE WORLD AND--
PING!
OH MY GOSH! HAVE YOU GUYS SEEN WHAT STEPHANIE JUST POSTED ABOUT CARLA?!
NO, WHAT?!
NO WAY!
I CAN'T BELIEVE HER...
HONESTLY, I'M LITERALLY NOT EVEN SURPRISED.

LIVE
1.5K

Goodnight sweetheart. Get a good night sleep for your studies tomorrow. Love mama and baba.

ZOOM
WHY DIDN'T I JUST SHUT UP? GOD! THEY PROBABLY THINK I'M JUST SOME LOUD-MOUTHED AMERICAN.
THEY ASKED YOU A QUESTION. THEY WERE BEING NICE AND YOU JUST... WHY IS IT SO HARD TO JUST SAY HELLO?!
PLUS I REALLY PUT MY FOOT IN IT WITH ANDI **AND** JEN. STUPID PHONE! THEY BOTH PROBABLY HATE ME...
STUPID! WAIT... IT'S OK. I WENT. I TALKED. I TRIED.

...OK TASH.
YOU TRY AGAIN
NEXT TIME.
...I'LL
GO AND TRY
IT AGAIN...
...JUST TRY
AGAIN...

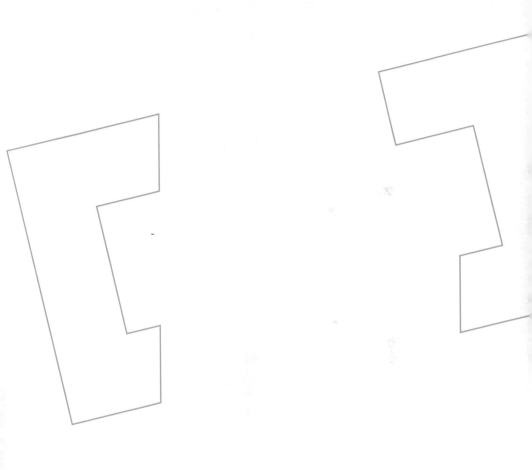

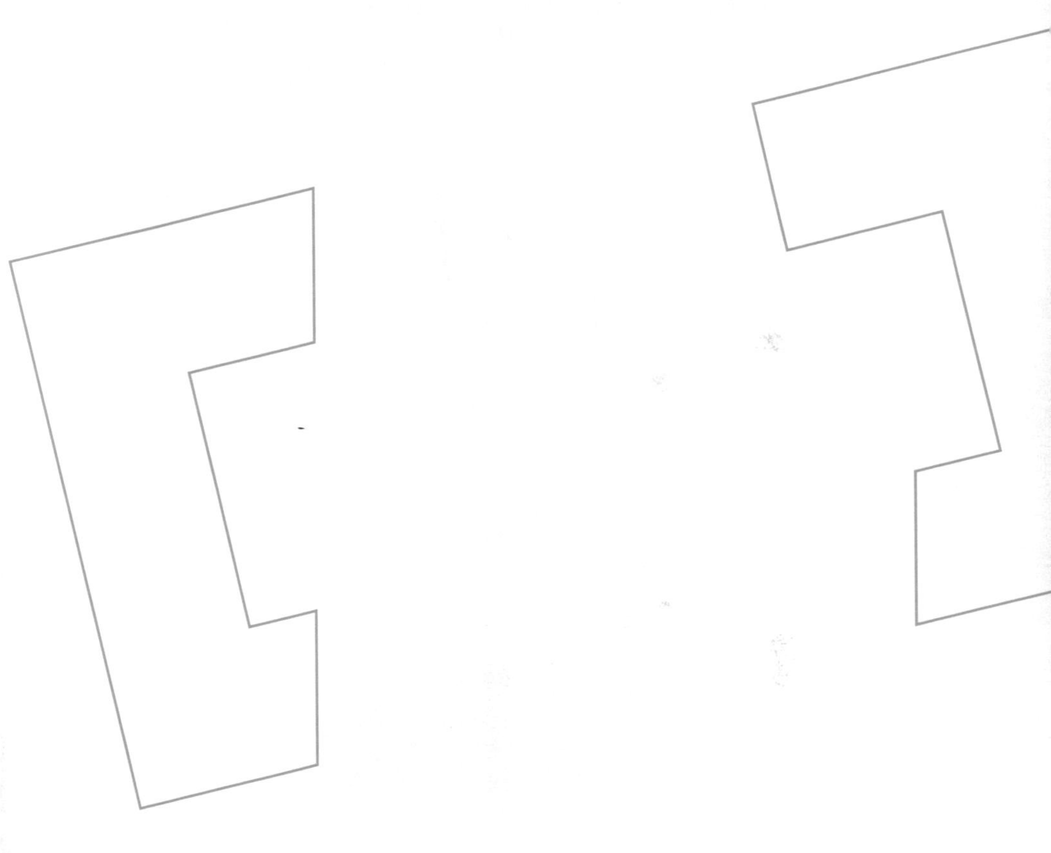

This space has been left for you.

STAGE TWO

TO DREAM

"THERE ARE NO NEW IDEAS. THERE ARE ONLY NEW WAYS OF MAKING THEM FELT." AUDRE LORDE*

*AUDRE LORDE WAS AN AMERICAN WRITER, FEMINIST, WOMANIST, LIBRARIAN, AND CIVIL RIGHTS ACTIVIST.

TODAY WE ARE GOING TO EXPLORE OUR DREAMS AND HOW HAVING THE AUDACITY TO DREAM IN THE FIRST PLACE IS A HUGE STEP FORWARD.
YOUR DREAM IS YOUR GUIDING LIGHT. THIS CAN MEAN VARIOUS THINGS TO DIFFERENT PEOPLE.

A WAY TO SEE THROUGH THE DARK.

A GOAL TO REACH FOR AGAINST ALL ODDS.

THE BEST WAY FORWARD FOR YOU.
ST JAMES

THE FUTURE WE CAN BUILD FOR OURSELVES.

A PATH TO FOLLOW TO LEAVE OUR MISTAKES BEHIND.

A FEELING OF HOPE WHEN WE'RE UP AGAINST THE WORST OF THINGS.

A WAY OUT OF WHERE WE ARE, INTO SOMETHING BETTER.

BEING A GUIDE TO OTHERS IN TIMES OF NEED.

START POINT 1

DREAM YOUR DREAM

DISCOVER WHAT'S IN YOUR HEART

OK, LET'S KEEP IT GOING, DO SOMETHING A LITTLE SCARY AND GET DEEP. WHAT'S IN YOUR HEART?
...
ERM...
BLOOD, I'D HOPE.
...
HA!
HEY ANDI. I'M SORRY ABOUT GETTING YOUR NAME WRONG THE OTHER DAY.
THAT'S OK... *TRISH.*
HA HA HA HA HA HA HA HA HA HA
I WANT EACH OF YOU TO THINK OF WHAT INSPIRES YOU. WHAT MAKES YOU FEEL HAPPY AND ENERGETIC?
OF ALL THE THINGS YOU ENJOY DOING, WHAT LIES IN EACH OF YOUR HEARTS?

THINK ABOUT THINGS, GOALS AND CLUES

THIS WILL HELP YOU FOCUS YOUR IDEAS

THIS IS TOUGH.
IT'S EASIER WHEN YOUR MIND IS CLEAR.

TRY TAKING A DEEP BREATH EVERYONE, LET THE IDEAS COME TO YOU.

HERE ARE SOME BASIC STARTING POINTS TO HELP YOU THINK. FIRSTLY, WE HAVE *THINGS.*
WHATS IN YOUR HEART
-THINGS
-GOALS
-CLUES

THESE CAN BE IMMEDIATE DREAMS THAT COME TO MIND, LIKE BECOMING A SINGER, COMEDIAN, DESIGNER, DOCTOR...
THINGS

DOES IT MATTER IF WE WRITE MORE THAN ONE IDEA?

THE MORE THE BETTER! WRITING THEM ALL DOWN WILL HELP COLLECT YOUR THOUGHTS.

AT WHAT POINT DO I GET TO START LISTING ALL THE SUPERHEROES I WANT TO BE?
WHICH SUPER-HEROES?
BATMAN, IRON MAN, SHARKBOY...
CAT WOMAN?
HELL YEAH!
MEOW
I'D LOOK WELL FIT IN A CATSUIT!
HA HA HA
GOALS
NEXT WE HAVE **GOALS.** THIS IS WHERE YOU CAN BE MORE SPECIFIC. THINK ABOUT WHERE IT IS YOU'D LIKE TO WORK OR BE.
IF YOU WERE A SINGER, WHERE WOULD YOU LIKE TO SING? IF YOU WERE A FASHION DESIGNER, WHO WOULD YOU DESIGN FOR?
BE BOLD IN YOUR DREAMING! THERE ARE NO BOUNDARIES FOR YOU TO WORRY ABOUT NOW.
ARTIST!
ANIMATOR
GAMES DESIGN?
"NEXT, I WANT YOU TO TAKE CLUES FROM YOUR LIFE. THINK ABOUT YOUR INTERESTS, YOUR TALENTS...
"...WHAT YOU'RE GOOD AT AND WHEN YOU HAVE BEEN HAPPY. THINK ABOUT WHEN YOU'VE BEEN YOUR BEST."
PROBLEM SOLVING
MATHS
SO, WE WRITE DOWN CLUES FROM WHEN WE'VE BEEN HAPPY OR FEEL GOOD?
YEAH, LIKE, I REALLY LOVE TALKING TO PEOPLE, SO I WROTE THAT DOWN.
REMEMBER, THIS IS ALL ABOUT YOU. FORGET WHERE YOU ARE AND DREAM.

THIS SPACE IS FOR YOUR REFLECTIONS | DATE: ....

WHAT THINGS DO YOU DREAM OF? WRITE THEM DOWN

These can be your immediate ideas: if you could do/be anything you want, what would it be? List the things that inspire you: e.g. singer, comedian, designer, doctor...

THIS SPACE IS FOR YOUR REFLECTIONS | DATE: ....

WHAT GOALS WOULD MAKE YOUR DREAM MORE SPECIFIC?

Can you be more specific about where you see yourself: who you'd like to work for, where and what you'd like to achieve?

THIS SPACE IS FOR YOUR REFLECTIONS / DATE: ....

WHAT ARE YOU GOOD AT OR ENJOY THE MOST?

This is the most important question. Take clues from your life: what are you interested in? What makes you happy? What or who inspires you? Where do your talents lie?

EXPLORING DIFFERENCES WILL HELP INSPIRE YOU

START POINT 2

USING EXTERNAL INSPIRATION

HAVE A BREAK FIRST!

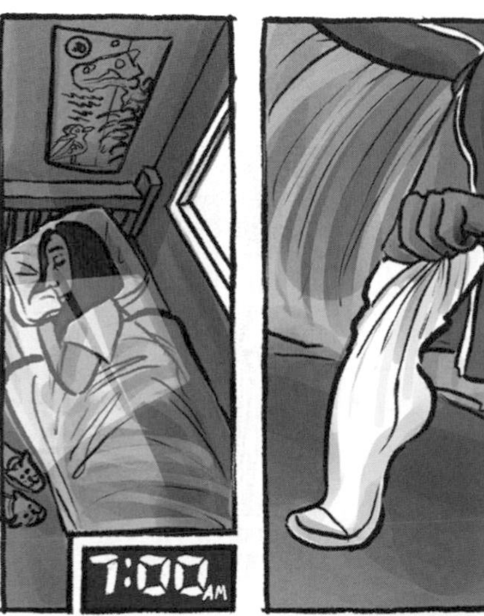

LET'S GO SAFARI

RESEARCH PLACES AND GO SOMEWHERE DIFFERENT

TALK TO DIFFERENT PEOPLE

ASK, LISTEN AND EXPLORE WHAT THEY THINK

ASKING QUESTIONS HELPS TO OPEN UP IDEAS

DON'T BE AFRAID TO ASK

IT'S ALL PART OF GROWING AND MOVING FORWARD

IMMERSE YOURSELF

IN DIFFERENT SPACES AND MEDIA

MH SMATHS

"MAGAZINES ARE A GREAT WAY TO EXPLORE DIFFERENT MEDIA SPACES. THE GUARDIAN AND BBC ARE GREAT AND FREE ONLINE. ALTHOUGH, BE WARY OF SOME SITES AS THERE'S LOTS OF CRAZY JUNK OUT THERE."

WHAT IF IT'S JUNK I'M INTO?
VOGE
YOU'LL JUST HAVE TO SWITCH IT UP.
WHY NOT TRY SOMETHING COMPLETELY NEW?
PFFFTT!
VOGE

"HAVE A GOOD LOOK AT THE SHELF. PICK SOMETHING THAT CATCHES YOUR EYE. THERE MAY BE SOME CLUES IN IT? WHY NOT TRY SOMETHING YOU'D NEVER NORMALLY PICK UP?

"WE ALL HAVE BIASES, SO LET'S CHALLENGE THEM."

WHY NOT EXPLORE?

USE DIFFERENT TOOLS AND RESOURCES AROUND YOU

"WHAT CAN YOU DO FOR A SAFARI? WRITE DOWN SOME IDEAS OF WHERE TO GO AND WHO YOU COULD GO WITH.

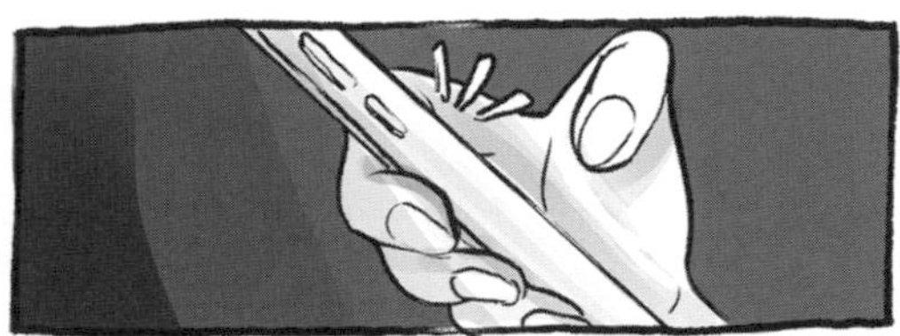

Hey Andi, it's Trish! ;) Just thought I'd text to say if you wanted to hang out sometime or need a tour from a 'local', let me know! x

THIS SPACE IS FOR YOUR REFLECTIONS | DATE: ....

WHERE COULD YOU GO FOR A SAFARI?

Which places seem interesting to you? Are there any you haven't been to before? Don't be afraid to try something new!

THIS SPACE IS FOR YOUR REFLECTIONS / DATE: ....

WHO COULD YOU TALK TO THAT MIGHT BE INTERESTING?

Where could you find interesting people? Perhaps in a library, museum, or in a place that interests you? Do you know anyone through family or friends?

THIS SPACE IS FOR YOUR REFLECTIONS | DATE: ....

WHAT MEDIA RESOURCES COULD BE HELPFUL FOR RESEARCHING?

Try reputable sources like the BBC website and iPlayer, The Guardian, magazines, books, blogs, TV documentaries and see what you find.

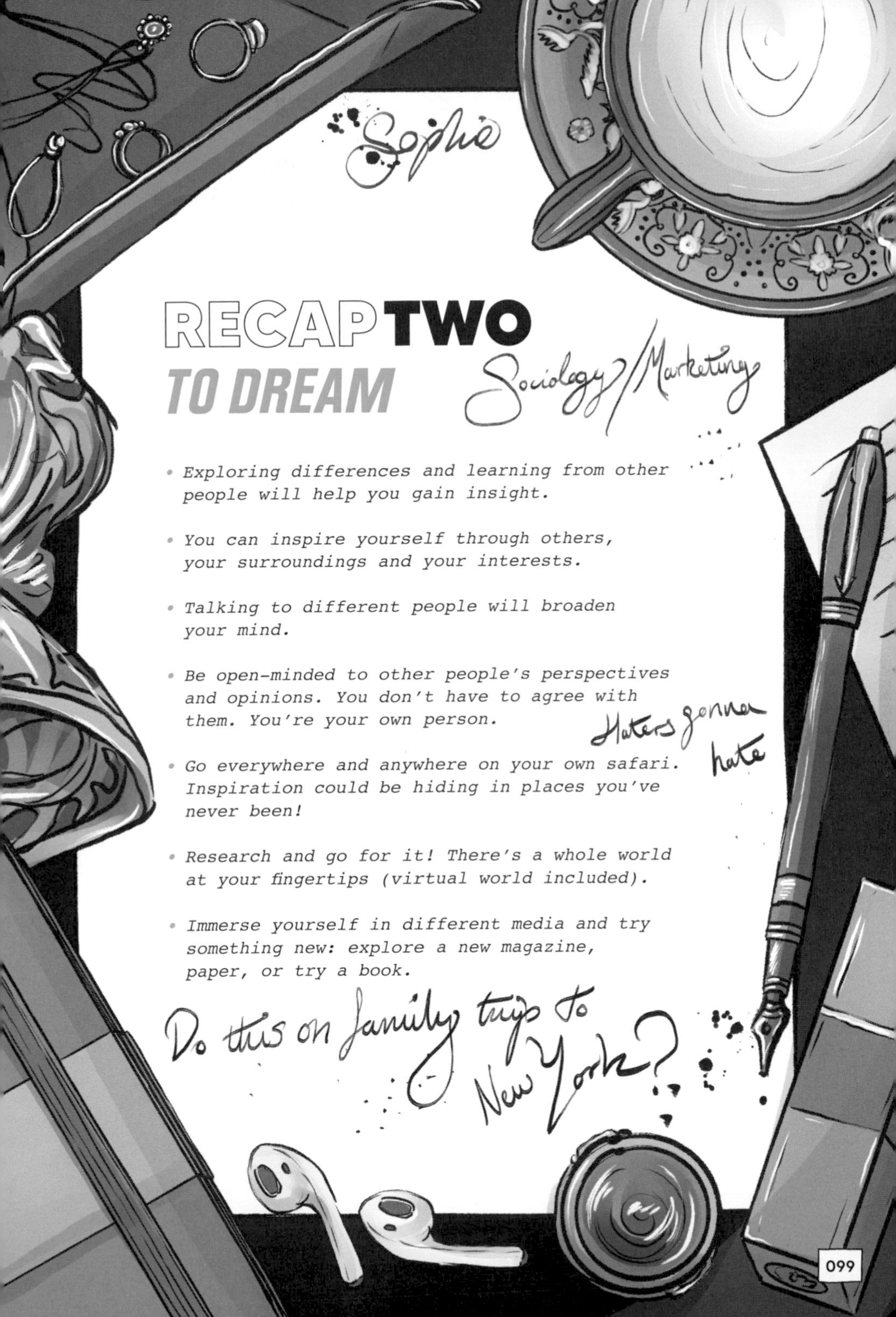

Sophie
Sociology/Marketing
Haters gonna hate
Do this on family trips to New York?

RECAP TWO TO DREAM

- *Exploring differences and learning from other people will help you gain insight.*
- *You can inspire yourself through others, your surroundings and your interests.*
- *Talking to different people will broaden your mind.*
- *Be open-minded to other people's perspectives and opinions. You don't have to agree with them. You're your own person.*
- *Go everywhere and anywhere on your own safari. Inspiration could be hiding in places you've never been!*
- *Research and go for it! There's a whole world at your fingertips (virtual world included).*
- *Immerse yourself in different media and try something new: explore a new magazine, paper, or try a book.*

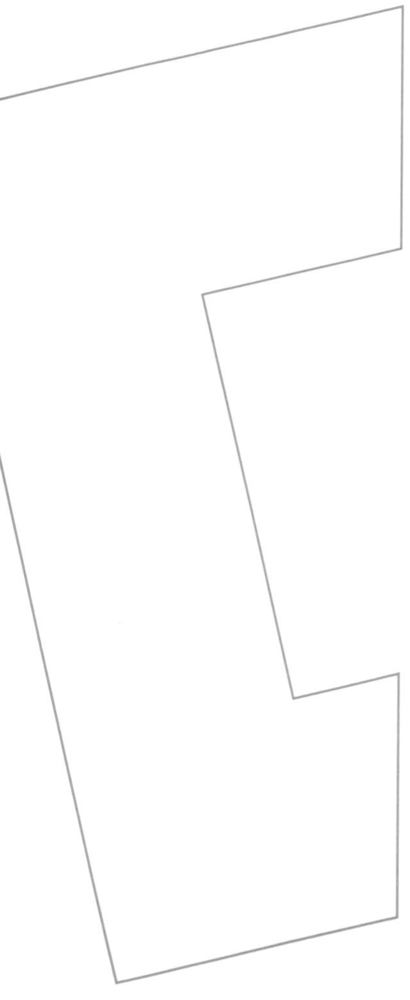

This space has been left for you.

ART UNI!
AUB
Falmouth
Leeds
UAL
NOTES!
YASMIN
YASMIN!
HEY, MOR, BABA. SO I WAS THINKING OF...*
*TRANSLATED FROM PASHTO.
JUST THE WOMAN WE WERE WAITING FOR!
WHY?
YOUR BABA'S GOT SOME EXCITING NEWS.
I MOST CERTAINLY DO!

NOW DON'T GET TOO EXCITED, BUT YOUR MOR AND I NOTICED HOW WELL YOU'VE BEEN DOING IN YOUR MATHS A LEVELS...

...AND YOUR TEACHER CALLED TODAY TO SAY YOU ARE ONE OF FIVE STUDENTS TO BE SELECTED FOR A HUGE OPPORTUNITY!

OH, JUST TELL HER, OMAR!

ONE OF THE SCHOOL'S GOVERNORS WORKS AT AN ACCOUNTANCY FIRM AND WANTS YOU TO INTERN WITH HIM!

MASHOOMA, IT'S A ***VERY BIG*** COMPANY. THIS WILL CHANGE YOUR ***LIFE.***

I--

NOW, THE TEACHER SAID YOU WILL HAVE TO MEET FOR AN INTERVIEW NEXT WEEK, SO IT'S NOT GUARANTEED YET...

BUT WITH YOUR MOR'S BEAUTY AND INTELLECT AND MY WITTY CHARM RUNNING THROUGH YOUR DNA...

OMAR!

...I DON'T SEE HOW YOU COULD FAIL.

Sigh

NOTES!

CHUCK

NOTES!

WELL DONE EVERYONE ON YOUR CASE STUDIES. THEY WERE ALL FANTASTIC.
ONE WAS PARTICULARLY EXEMPLARY AND I'D LIKE YOU ALL TO PAY CLOSE ATTENTION.

ANDI. HOW WOULD YOU FEEL ABOUT READING THE INTRODUCTION TO YOUR PIECE ON ENVIRONMENTAL DAMAGE IN ICELAND?
I, URM...

IF NOT, THEN PERHAPS YOU'D ALLOW ME TO READ IT OUT?

YOU'VE GOT THIS, GIRL! DON'T WORRY ABOUT YOUR ENGLISH!

IT- IT'S OK. I'LL DO IT.

...AND BECAUSE OF THEIR NATURAL RESOURCES, ICELAND'S MAN-OU-VERA...
...THEIR M-MAN-OU-VERABILTY... THEIR...
IDIOT! WHY ARE YOU DOING THIS?!

!
tap tap

HEY THERE! I'M LUCIE. ANDI, RIGHT?
UH, YEAH?

I RUN THE ENVIRONMENTAL CLUB. WE'VE GOT A TRIP TO ICELAND COMING UP.
YOUR GEOGRAPHY TEACHER MENTIONED YOU DID THIS INSANELY GOOD CASE STUDY ON IT AND I WAS WONDERING IF YOU'D BE INTERESTED IN JOINING?
5:30 Thursday Block C Room 3
THE GREEN SOC!
GS

5:30 Thursday Block C Room 3
THE GREEN SOC!

OF COURSE, YOU'D HAVE TO JOIN THE CLUB AND I GET YOU MIGHT NOT ACTUALLY CARE. I JUST THOUGHT--

NO, ***NO,*** I MEAN, ***YES!*** I MEAN...

...I DO CARE. I'D LOVE TO JOIN.

GREAT! FAB! SEE YOU THERE, THEN!

N-***ICE*** ONE ME...

C Block Level 1
Rooms 1 – 6 →
← Toilets
OK, HERE WE GO...
5:30
Thursday
Block C
Room 3
THE GREEN

...BREATHE...
...SHE ASKED YOU TO COME. YOU WERE **INVITED.** NO NEED TO STRESS.

JUST SHOW UP. YOU DON'T EVEN HAVE TO TALK TO ANYONE. IT'LL BE GOOD.

OH GOD, BUT WHAT IF SOMEONE FROM YOUR CLASS IS THERE?
NO. THAT'S FINE. WHY WOULD THAT MATTER?

THEY MIGHT RECOGNISE YOU AND MAKE FUN OF YOUR SPEECH FROM EARLIER.
I BET LUCY WILL BRING IT UP WHEN SHE INTRODUCES YOU AS WELL!

THERE ARE SO MANY PEOPLE! THERE'S BOUND TO BE SOME OF YOUR CLASS HERE!

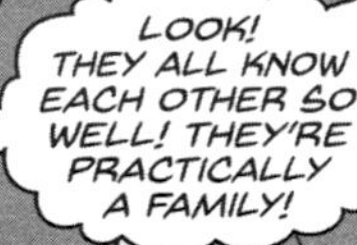
LOOK! THEY ALL KNOW EACH OTHER SO WELL! THEY'RE PRACTICALLY A FAMILY!

GREEN SOC!
Register

IDIOT. LOSER. CAN'T TALK IN FRONT OF PEOPLE. CAN'T EVEN WALK INTO A ROOM WITH **STRANGERS** ANYMORE.
IT'S **PATHETIC. YOU'RE PATHETIC.**

& Mile
OK. STOP. IT'S OK. YOU'RE OK. (RE)START. YOU WENT TO (RE)START. AND YOU MADE A FRIEND. WE CAN STILL WIN TODAY.

tap tap tap xap tap tap xap tap
Andi
Hey trish! Fancy going to a comedy night?

Ring! Ring
LET'S DO IT! WHEN D'YOU HAVE IN MIND?

SO, ANDI... EVER BEEN TEMPTED TO GO UP THERE AND DO A SET?
Comedy NIGH
OH NO, NO. NO. I COULDN'T. I'D DIE.

BUT YOU'RE SO FUNNY! AND YOU DON'T SEEM THAT SHY?
NO. I'M SUPER SHY. ZERO CONFIDENCE.
PLUS, I'M TERRIBLE AT PUBLIC SPEAKING.

I GET THE PUBLIC SPEAKING THING. A TOP TIP THAT WORKED FOR ME WHEN I USED TO DO THEATRE BACK IN THE US WAS TO JUST IMAGINE EVERYONE AS SHEEP. HONEST TO GOD, IT WORKS.

AND I DON'T BELIEVE YOU'RE THAT SHY. I MEAN YOU WENT TO (RE)START, RIGHT? ***AND*** YOU REACHED OUT TO ME. A LOT OF PEOPLE WOULDN'T BE ABLE TO DO THAT.

SOPHIE, I'VE TOLD YOU BEFORE TO TURN THAT GHASTLY NOISE OFF. YOU'LL DISTRACT YOUR SISTER FROM HER PRACTICE.

EE 19:19 49%
beauties
Daniel, Meg, You and 32 others...
Clara created group "beauties <3"
Clara
hi beauties! so me and george have been dating 1 gorgeous year now and we want to celebrate it with all our gorgeous friends! (i.e. you!!) The barringtons are hosting<333 6:30pm friday, plus ones welcome xxx

Priya (restart)

got this party friday, wondering if u wanted to come with, provide some moral support?? xxx

PLEASE MA?*

I DON'T THINK SO.

SOMEPLACE IN SURREY? THE COUNTRYSIDE?!

THAT'S AWFULLY FAR AWAY, PUTTAR. BESIDES, WE'VE FAMILY DINNER ON FRIDAY.

WHY DON'T YOU ASK JAIDEEP TO HELP FOR ONCE?

*TRANSLATED FROM PUNJABI.

PRIYA, YOU KNOW YOUR BROTHER'S NO GOOD IN THE KITCHEN. HE'LL PROBABLY BE OUT ANYWAY.

WELL, **TOUGH SHIT,** COS THIS TIME I'M GOING TO BE OUT AS WELL.

see you there friday! xx

FRIDAY

OK, WOW. **THIS** IS POSH.

C'MON, SOPHIE. WHERE THE **HEL**L ARE YOU?

SHIT.
ALERT DANGER
BLOOD SUGAR CRITICAL

DOUBLE SHIT.
PING
Sophie
Hey hun I'm SO sorry but I'm running late! see you soon! xxx

C'MON, IT **HAS** TO BE IN HERE...

URM, HELLO THERE. I'M STANLEY BARRINGTON-SMYTH. CAN I HELP YOU?

OH! UH... HI! I'M PRIYA, SOPHIE'S MATE.
OH, I SEE. YOU'RE SOPHIE'S FRIEND. OF COURSE YOU ARE.
ARE YOU OK? YOU LOOK RATHER FLUSHED.

ACTUALLY, I'M, UH, FEELING PRETTY ILL...
...AND I THINK I'VE LEFT MY INSULIN KIT AT HOME.

OH DEAR! YOU POOR THING.
PERHAPS WE CAN FETCH YOU SOMETHING? A SICK BUCKET?

URM, NO THAT'S OK, THANKS. I THINK I NEED TO GO BACK HOME FOR IT...
...BUT, TO BE HONEST, I'M A BIT WORRIED I WON'T MAKE IT BACK IN TIME.

NOT TO WORRY, I'LL CALL YOU A TAXI IMMEDIATELY. I'M SURE THAT'S THE BEST OPTION.
OH, ACTUALLY--

...I'M NOT SURE IF--
THAT'S OK! I'LL HAVE THIS DONE IN A JIFFY!

STANLEY WILL CALL HIS USUAL DRIVER. HE'S A DELIGHTFUL MAN. HE'LL LOOK AFTER YOU.

THANKS, BUT I'M NOT SURE THAT--
OH, HOLD ON, PRIJA.
SOMEONE'S JUST ARRIVED WHO I ABSOLUTELY NEED TO SEE.
GWENDALYN, DARLING!

...DAMN IT.

tap
tap
TAP

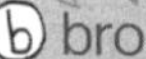
PING

b bro

hey jai.
i really need a lift home. it's an emergency. pls.
(1 min ago)

sorry pri, am busy atm, jus call papa or ma.
(just now)

BOOM

TAXI

!

WHAT HAS GOTTEN INTO YOU?! ONCE WE GET YOU BETTER, YOUR PAPA AND I WILL BE HAVING WORDS WITH YOU. HONESTLY...*
*TRANSLATED FROM PUNJABI.

...RUNNING OFF TO PARTIES, GETTING EXPENSIVE TAXIS, ENDANGERING YOURSELF! PERHAPS WE'LL HAVE TO RECONSIDER THE SORT OF THINGS THIS NEW COURSE IS TEACHING YOU.

SOOO BEA, DO YOU THINK YOU'LL CHAT TO GEORGE TODAY?
OH, I DON'T KNOW...
TAXI

Scream
OH, GO ON, BEA. DON'T BE SUCH A BITCH ABOUT IT.
WE ALL KNOW HOW THE NIGHT WILL END.
Sophie
Hey hun, we're here! xxx

Smek
OH, SOPHIE. WE MET YOUR FRIEND... WHAT WAS HER NAME?

PRIJA!
DO YOU MEAN PRIYA?
YES.

POOR GIRL WAS FEELING ILL SO WE PUT HER IN A TAXI HOME.
YES, STANLEY AND I LOOKED AFTER HER. SHE LEFT LITERALLY WITHIN FIVE MINUTES OF ARRIVAL. QUITE ODD.

SHE REALLY REMINDED ME OF THAT

Hey hun my friends said you were ill and went home? r u ok? Xx
(43 mins ago)
What's going on? why not say you left?
(21 mins ago)
??? Xx
(just now)

...S O P H I E...

...HELLLLOOO!
EARTH TO SOPHIE.
OH, UM, SORRY, YEAH?

BABE, YOU KNOW STARING AT YOUR PHONE ISN'T GOING TO MAKE HER RESPOND. WHAT'S UP WITH YOU RECENTLY? YOU'VE BEEN SO SCATTY.
SIP

SORRY, JUST HAVE A LOT GOING ON...

SHE'S JUST BITTER BECAUSE HER COOL NEW FRIEND DITCHED HER AND NOW SHE'S STUCK WITH US.

THAT...
...THAT'S NOT TRUE!
BABE, IT'S OK. YOU CAN BE HONEST. WE'D JUST LIKE YOU TO TELL US ABOUT YOUR TWO-FACED PLAN TO SLOWLY REPLACE US IS ALL.

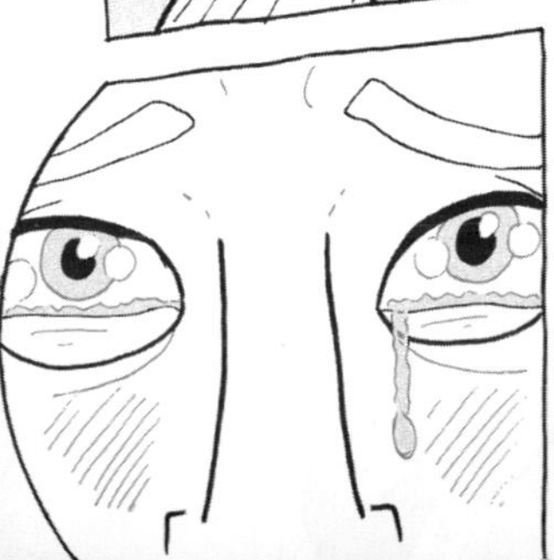

DANIEL, TELL HER YOU'RE JOKING!
OH, COME ON, SOPHIE. HE'S CLEARLY JOKING.

TO MY BOY NATE FOR TRICKING SOME SUCKERS INTO SIGNING HIM!
AND TO CLARE. CONGRATS ON YOUR PLACE AT UNI TO START A REAL CAREER! (JUST KIDDING, NATE!)
WELL DONE, GIRL. I'M SO PROUD OF YOU!
PEK!
THANKS, BABE.
SO, TASH, HAVE YOU THOUGHT ANYMORE ABOUT YOUR NEXT STEPS?
YEAH, ACTUALLY. I WAS KINDA THINKING BACK TO MY THEATRE DAYS IN THE US. THOUGHT MAYBE DOING SOMETHING LIKE THAT--
WHAT, LIKE AN ACTOR?!
UH, WELL, MAYBE NOT. I GUESS MORE LIKE A TALK SHOW HOST OR SOMETHING? I JUST FEEL LIKE I'D BE GOOD AT THAT SORT OF--
HOW THE HELL DO YOU BECOME A TALK SHOW HOST?

DON'T YOU HAVE TO BE, LIKE, UNBELIEVABLY PRETTY AND CHARISMATIC FOR THAT?

WELL, LIKE, MAYBE NOT THAT SPECIFICALLY...

NO, I GET WHAT YOU MEAN.

LIKE, I CAN TOTALLY IMAGINE YOU AS AN INFLUENCER.
THAT'S NOT REALLY WHAT I MEAN EITHER--
?
?
LIKE AN INSTA BADDIE! SIS!

YEAH! OR LIKE A PERSONAL SHOPPER, KINDA LIKE YOU DO NOW?
WHAT'S THIS? TASH IS DOING FASHION?

YEAH, BABES.
I CAN SEE THAT! OR LIKE AN INFLUENCER MAYBE?
THAT'S WHAT I SAID!
HUN! YOU'VE ALREADY GOT SO MANY FOLLOWERS!

:48
Instagrim
Dean_T
lose.it.lollipops
Sponsored
Lose it Lollipops
Learn More
Lose.it.lollipops Brand new
SCROLL

Brand new
View comments

00:52
Comm
tashpanda
A taste of home
the american sty
diner time. Drinks
#memories #shakes

om? i love it!
2m Reply
ninahartssx SO FIT <3
2m Reply
aimee_57 omg looks so yum!
7m Reply
damon459 fat ugly bitch
6m Reply

ollykillz ugh! need to go here
22m Reply
omment as tashpanda...

fat ugly bitch

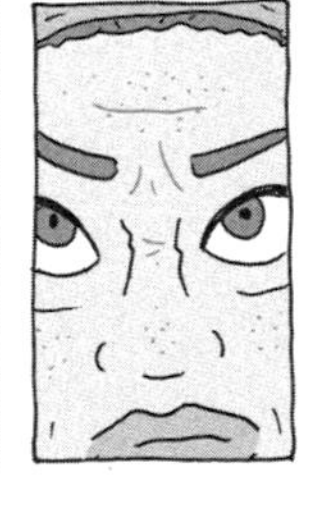

Sigh

power off
SLIDE

SLAM

Ping

Inbox(1)
in
oble.com/mail/u/0/#

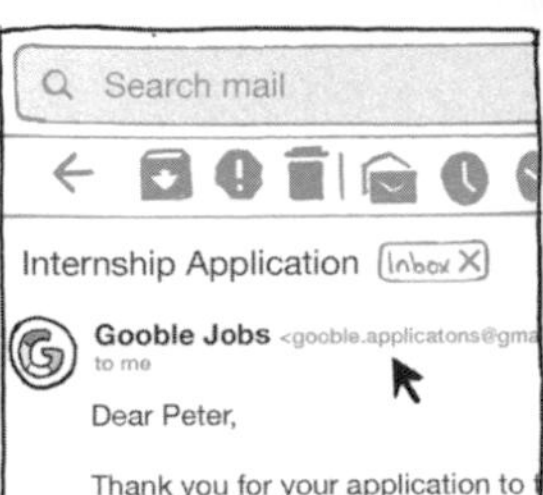
Search mail
Internship Application
Inbox
Gooble Jobs <gooble.applicatons@gma
to me
Dear Peter,
Thank you for your application to
We're pleased to inform you that y
The interview will involve a short 5

YES.
YES! MUM!

I GOT IT! I GOT THE INTERVIEW!

MUM...?

ST JAMES SCHOOL

SLUMP!

YOU GOT THE INTERVIEW?!
THAT'S AWESOME! CONGRATS, PETEY BOI! BET YOU'RE GLAD YOU LISTENED TO ME ABOUT APPLYING, EH?

YOU LOOK SAD. WHAT'S UP, BIG MAN?
HEH, YEAH...

THE INTERVIEW... I'VE GOTTA DO THIS WHOLE RESEARCH PRESENTATION THING, WHICH IS FINE! JUST WITH MY MUM GETTING SICK AN ALL...

...I DON'T KNOW IF I'LL HAVE THE TIME TO PREPARE FOR IT.

OR, HECK, WHETHER I SHOULD DO IT AT ALL OR JUST GET AN ACTUAL JOB.
OIII! NAH, MATE. **NAH.** YOU'RE DOING IT.
EVEN IF I HAVE TO COME TO YOUR HOUSE AND DO THE BLOODY THING WITH YOU.

IS THAT AN OFFER?
WELL, IF PETEY BOI REALLY NEEDS BIG DADDY TEEJ TO HOLD HIS HAND TO GET THROUGH THIS...
...THEN YEAH.

ALL RIGHT, MATE. YOU'RE ON.
!

I LOOK FORWARD TO A LONG AND SUCCESSFUL BUSINESS RELATIONSHIP WITH YOU, MY FINE GENTLE-MAN.
SLOW DOWN, TJ MAXX. IT'S JUST A PRESENTATION.

ARGH! SORRY, G.
ONE SEC, JUST GOTTA SIT DOWN FOR A MIN.

ON FIELDS
London Borough of Hackney
Mentmore Terrace
YOU OK?
YEAH, MAN. IT'S CALM. IT JUST FLARES UP SOMETIMES.
WHAT HAPPENED TO IT?
hop hop hop

SPORTS INJURY.
OH YEAH? DIDN'T KNOW YOU WERE AN ATHLETE! WHAT KIND OF SPORTS?
PLONK

I'M MORE THAN JUST A PRETTY FACE!
RAN TRACK AND FIELD. USED TO TRAIN TWICE DAILY...

...NOT SINCE I FUCKED MY ANKLE THOUGH...
London Borough of Hackney
Mentmore Terrace

WHEN'S IT GONNA GET BETTER?
I DUNNO... I'VE GOTTA GET THIS OPERATION. I COULD ACTUALLY BOOK IN MY DATE WHENEVER I WANT.
BUT THE REHAB AFTERWARDS TAKES MONTHS, AND I AIN'T READY TO BE ON CRUTCHES FOR MONTHS, Y'KNOW? IT'S A PRETTY SCARY COMMITMENT.

BUT YOU CAN'T DO SPORTS AGAIN UNTIL YOU GET THE OPERAT-ION?

YEAH, MAN. IT'S SHIT.

WE AREN'T FAR FROM MY PLACE NOW. LET'S STOP BY THERE BEFORE YOU GO BACK AND WE CAN PUT SOME ICE ON IT?

YEAH... THANKS, FAM. THAT WOULD ACTUALLY BE IDEAL.

OI! STOP WHERE YOU ARE.
WHAT'S GOING ON HERE, LADS?
WHAT THE...?
WE'RE GOING HOME, OFFICER. WE'VE BEEN OUT AT A WORK EVENT.
POLICE
A WORK EVENT, EH? WHO'S BEEN WITH YOU?
WHAT'S GOING ON, BRUV? WHY YOU STOPPING US?
IT'S A JOKE, MATE.
WE'RE JUST STANDING.
ALL RIGHT, SON.
I HAVE REASON TO SUSPECT THAT YOU'RE IN POSSESSION OF CONTRA-BAND.
THIS IS A SECTION 60 AREA. I WILL NOW CONDUCT A STOP AND SEARCH.
SORRY! PLEASE IGNORE MY FRIEND, OFFICERS. I'M SO SORRY.
WE'RE DOING A SELF-DEVELOPMENT COURSE.
WE HUNG BACK LATE TODAY TO CHAT TO OUR TUTORS AND ARE JUST WALKING HOME.
I CAN GIVE YOU THEIR CONTACT DETAILS IF YOU'D LIKE TO CONFIRM WITH THEM?
IS THAT TRUE?
ERM, YES OFFICER, MA'AM.

VERY WELL. ON YOUR WAY, LADS.
I DON'T WANT TO SEE YOU LURKING AROUND HERE AGAIN.
YOU GOT THAT?
POLICE

SLUMP
DUDE... I CAN'T **BELIEVE** YOU!

THAT WAS SOME **BULLSHIT.**
Pace

WAIT...
WHAT'RE YOU ON ABOUT? WHAT'D I DO?
ARE YOU INSANE?! YOU DON'T SPEAK TO POLICE LIKE THAT! WE WERE NEARLY ARRESTED!
OI! CHILL, YEAH. THEY CAME AT **US.** IT'S NOT MY FAULT I'M FROM THE ENDS.
AND WHERE THE **FUCK** DO YOU THINK I'M FROM? YOU THINK I DON'T DEAL WITH THIS EVERY OTHER **DAMN WEEK?**
...
SHIT, TJ...
...YOU CAN'T ACT LIKE THAT--
GASP
--WHO WOULD LOOK AFTER MY BROTHERS--
GASP
--IF I WAS ARRESTED--
GASP
--HUH?

HEY, I'M SORRY FAM. I DIDN'T MEAN TO PISS YOU OFF...
....YOU OK?
...IT'S FINE--
GASP
--A PANIC ATTACK--
GASP
--JUST GO HOME--
GASP
LOOK, I REALLY AM SORRY I GOT ANGRY. I KNOW I SHOULDN'T OF... I'M JUST FED UP WITH EVERYONE TREATIN' ME LIKE A WASTEMAN, Y'KNOW?
DO YOU NEED AN AMBULANCE OR SOMETHING? MAYBE I COULD--
PLEASE! JUST GO HOME, TJ.
GASP
I'M FINE--
GASP
GASP
GASP

...
CLICK
YO, MUMSY...
...YOU OK?
TJ! I'M OK, THANK YOU. HOW WAS YOUR CLASS TODAY?
URM IT'S MORE OF A COURSE BUT UH, YEAH, IT WAS GOOD, THANKS...
...SOO, WHATCHA DOIN'?
JUST SOME FUN MONEY STUFF. YOU KNOW, SORTING THINGS OUT...
SNATCH
...INTO ORDERED PILES.

HEY, MUM...
...WHAT HAPPENED TO YOUR NECK?
OH NOTHING, JUST UM--
WAS IT BARRY?
NO, TJ IT WASN'T **BARRY.** IT'S FUNNY ACTUALLY... IT WAS MY FAULT, YOU SEE. JUST AN ACCIDENT...

WHERE IS HE NOW?
HE'S JUST POPPED OUT DOWN THE PUB FOR A BIT BUT PLEASE, TJ, TRUST ME. HE DIDN'T DO ANYTHING. HE WOULDN'T HURT A FLY--
WOULDN'T HURT A ***FLY?!*** WHAT ABOUT THE TIME HE...

Sigh
...IT'S OK, MUM. I WON'T SAY ANYTHING TO HIM.

JUST... MAYBE WE COULD FIND SOME HELP FOR YOU?

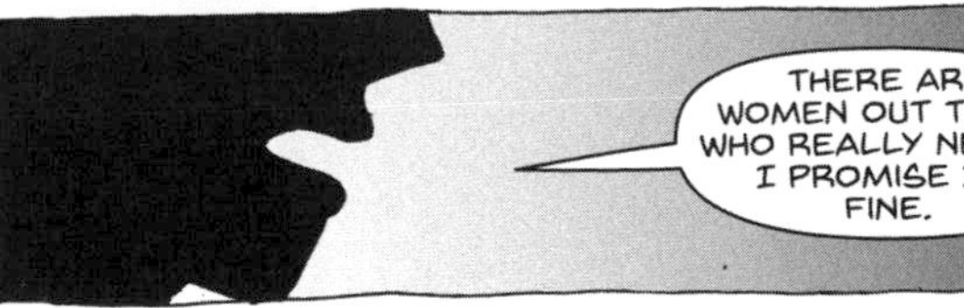

THERE ARE WOMEN OUT THERE WHO REALLY NEED IT. I PROMISE I'M FINE.

OK.
BUT YOU KNOW I'M ALWAYS HERE FOR YOU, YEAH?

YOU KNOW YOU'RE A REAL SWEETHEART, TJ. I LOVE YOU SO MUCH.

LOVE YOU TOO, MUM.

STAGE THREE

KNOW YOURSELF

"AS LONG AS I HOLD FAST TO MY BELIEFS AND VALUES, AND FOLLOW MY OWN MORAL COMPASS, THEN THE ONLY EXPECTATIONS I NEED TO LIVE UP TO ARE MY OWN."

MICHELLE OBAMA*

*MICHELLE OBAMA WAS THE FIRST AFRICAN-AMERICAN FIRST LADY OF THE UNITED STATES.

KNOWING YOUR VALUES

GIVES YOU CLARITY ON WHAT YOU STAND FOR

SHALL WE TALK VALUES? WHAT DO YOU ALL THINK YOUR VALUES ARE?

LET'S DISCUSS AS A GROUP. THINK ALONG THE LINES OF YOUR BASIC OR FUNDAMENTAL BELIEFS.

SO, STUFF THAT GUIDES OR MOTIVATES OUR ACTIONS?
YEAH, OR OUR ATTITUDES. SO, LIKE, THINGS THAT HELP US DETERMINE WHAT'S IMPORTANT TO US. AND I GUESS WHAT'S NOT, TOO.
OUR VALUES ARE OUR CORE BELIEFS. WHAT WE STAND BY.
I GUESS MOST PEOPLE MAYBE HAVEN'T REALLY THOUGHT ABOUT THEIR VALUES BEFORE...
...BUT MIGHT STILL HAVE AN IDEA OF WHAT THEY STAND FOR AS A PERSON?

SOME PEOPLE HAVE STRONG VALUES FROM THEIR FAMILY, RELIGION OR LIFE EXPERIENCES, AND OTHER PEOPLE NOT SO MUCH...
I'VE NEVER GIVEN IT MUCH THOUGHT...

WISE WORDS, EVERYONE. YOU'VE PRETTY MUCH COVERED ALL THE DEFINITIONS!

MAKING DECISIONS THAT FIT WITH OUR VALUES SHOULD HELP US BE HAPPY AND FULFILLED AS WE MOVE TOWARDS OUR DREAMS.

IF YOU FIND YOURSELF DOING THINGS THAT YOU FEEL PRESSURED TO DO AND IT DOESN'T FEEL RIGHT - IT COULD BE BECAUSE YOU'RE SACRIFICING YOUR VALUES.

!
OK, EVERYONE. LET'S GET ON OUR FEET.
WE'RE GOING TO TAKE A LITTLE WALK.

HEY, ANDI. I KNOW SHARING WITH THE GROUP MUST BE A PRETTY SCARY THING TO DO, BUT THESE LAST FEW WEEKS YOU'VE REALLY STARTED COMING OUT OF YOUR SHELL. MAYBE YOU'RE JUST TIRED TODAY...

...BUT YOU KNOW THIS IS A SAFE SPACE, AND WE'D REALLY LOVE TO HEAR WHAT ANDI THINKS EVERY NOW AND AGAIN. CAN YOU MAKE THAT HAPPEN?
YEAH. SURE.

GREAT. NOW LET'S GO FIND OUT WHAT MYSTERIOUS DERELICT BUILDING WE'RE LEADING YOU TO...
GOOD JOB I'VE HAD MY TETANUS SHOT.

YOUR VALUES

WILL HELP YOU MAKE THE RIGHT DECISIONS

FANTASTIC WORK, EVERY-ONE.
NOW, IF YOU'D HUMOUR MO AND I, WE'D EACH LIKE TO TELL YOU GUYS A LITTLE STORY.

"I GREW UP IN A SMALL TOWN IN THE NORTH OF ENGLAND. MY GRANDFATHER AND FATHER WERE BOTH MINERS.

OUR VALUES

KEEP US TRUE TO OURSELVES

"IT WAS A TIGHT-KNIT COMMUNITY WHERE PEOPLE HAD TO STICK TOGETHER AND HELP EACH OTHER OUT.

"EVERYONE WORKED HARD. USUALLY IN DANGEROUS CONDITIONS MILES UNDER-GROUND IN THE DARK AND HOT MINES. GROWING UP IN THIS COMMUNITY MEANT I LEARNT TO VALUE HONESTY, COMPASSION, AND HUMILITY.

"BEFORE ME, NO ONE FROM MY FAMILY HAD GONE TO UNIVERSITY. BUT I WAS VERY FORTUNATE TO BECOME GOOD AT SCHOOL AND RECEIVED OFFERS FROM SEVERAL UNIVERSITIES."

"THE INTERVIEWS WERE TOUGH. ESPECIALLY AT OXFORD. A FEW PEOPLE EVEN POKED FUN AT MY ACCENT AND LOOKED DOWN ON ME BECAUSE OF WHERE I WAS FROM. THIS ENVIRONMENT DIDN'T ALIGN WITH THE VALUES I'D BEEN BROUGHT UP WITH.

"THIS ULTIMATELY LED TO ME CHOOSING WARWICK INSTEAD.

"WHILE I WAS THERE, I SAW AN AMAZING OPPORTUNITY FOR A SCHOLARSHIP TO HARVARD UNIVERSITY IN AMERICA.
"EAGER FOR A NEW EXPERIENCE, I APPLIED AND GOT THROUGH TO THE FIRST ROUND OF INTERVIEWS. IN THE WAITING ROOM I ENDED UP TALKING TO THE RECEPTIONIST. I WAS SO NERVOUS, BUT SHE WAS REALLY KIND. AT THE TIME I DIDN'T THINK ANYTHING OF IT. I WAS JUST LIVING BY MY VALUES.

"IT LATER TURNED OUT THAT SHE WAS ON THE SELECTION COMMITTEE AND OUT OF THE ONE HUNDRED APPLICANTS ONLY ME AND ONE OTHER GIRL HAD BOTHERED TO TALK TO HER.

"THIS LED TO US BOTH GETTING A SCHOLARSHIP TO HARVARD, WHICH LED TO WHERE I AM TODAY. WHILE I HAD AIMS, MUCH OF IT WASN'T PLANNED. I SIMPLY STUCK TO MY VALUES AS I PURSUED MY DREAMS AND SEIZED OPPORTUNITIES. YOU SEE, WE ALL HAVE THE POWER TO CHOOSE THE VALUES WE WANT...
"...AND IT'S UP TO US TO CHOOSE WHAT TYPE OF PERSON WE WANT TO BE. AND IF YOU STICK TO YOUR VALUES, THINGS HAVE A FUNNY WAY OF WORKING OUT IN YOUR FAVOUR."

THANK YOU, JEN. NOW TO SHARE A LITTLE STORY OF MY OWN.

"MY FAITH HELPS GUIDE MY DECISION MAKING AND HELPS ME BECOME A BETTER PERSON. BUT WHEN I WAS YOUNGER, I WORRIED MY FAITH MIGHT PUT ME AT A DISADVANTAGE IN CERTAIN PLACES.
LONDON MOSQUE

BE TRUE TO YOURSELF

DON'T SACRIFICE YOUR VALUES

"LIKE AT A COMPUTING COMPANY I DID WORK EXPERIENCE FOR. I WAS JUST EIGHTEEN THEN. I'D ALWAYS ASPIRED TO WORK IN THAT INDUSTRY, SO I WANTED TO MAKE SURE EVERYONE THERE LIKED ME.

"BUT I KEPT DECLINING INVITES TO GO OUT FOR DRINKS. EVENTUALLY I TOLD MY COLLEAGUES THAT I'M MUSLIM AND I DON'T DRINK ALCOHOL. I THOUGHT THEY MIGHT BE ODD WITH ME.

"HOWEVER, THEY CHANGED PLANS TO ACCOMMODATE ME AND WE ALL WENT OUT FOR FOOD INSTEAD."

"IT WAS THEIR FIRST TIME EATING OUT TOGETHER AND WE ENDED UP TRYING A NEW RESTAURANT NEARBY. IT SOON BECAME A DEPARTMENT-WIDE FAVOURITE!
"WE HAD MANY OUTINGS OVER THE NEXT FEW MONTHS, AND I WAS OFFERED MENTORSHIPS AND ADVICE ON BECOMING A DESIGNER AND CODER.
"IF I HADN'T SHARED MY VALUES AND STUCK TO THEM, NONE OF THAT WOULD'VE HAPPENED.
"SURE, I FELT A BIT EXPOSED WHEN I TOLD THEM, BUT THEY WERE COMPLETELY FINE.
"AND REGARDLESS OF THE OUTCOME, I WOULD'VE COMPLETELY LET MYSELF DOWN IF I HADN'T STAYED TRUE TO MY VALUES."
OF COURSE, NOW IT'S ONLY FAIR THAT YOU GUYS GET TO EXPERIENCE THE VALUE OF A GOOD GROUP MEAL!
WHO'S FOR LUNCH?
YES!
I LOVE THIS COURSE.

OK, LET'S TAKE A SHEET OF PAPER, OR USE YOUR BOOKS.

BETWEEN THIS AND THE *SAFARI*, I THINK I MIGHT BE DEVELOPING TRUST ISSUES...
WRITE DOWN YOUR THOUGHTS TO THESE THREE QUESTIONS.

WHY NOT EXPLORE?

WHAT ARE YOUR VALUES?

"ONE: WHAT ARE YOUR VALUES? WRITE DOWN THE WORDS THAT DESCRIBE YOU. FOR EXAMPLE, I AM KIND, I AM COMPASSIONATE, I AM AMBITIOUS.

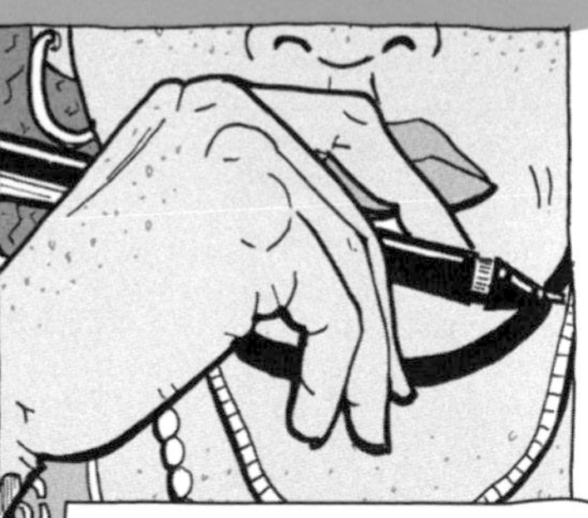

"TWO: NOW IMAGINE YOUR BEST FRIEND OR LOVED ONE IS MAKING A SPEECH ABOUT YOU AT YOUR BIRTHDAY PARTY. WHAT MIGHT THEY SAY ABOUT YOU? TAKE A FEW MINUTES TO IMAGINE THIS. CLOSE YOUR EYES IF IT HELPS. IMAGINE THE PLACE YOU'RE IN, THE PEOPLE THERE AND YOUR FRIEND. WHEN YOU'RE READY, WRITE IT DOWN."

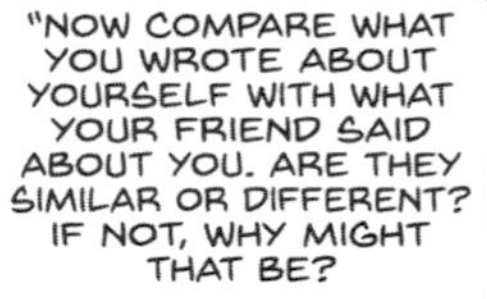
"NOW COMPARE WHAT YOU WROTE ABOUT YOURSELF WITH WHAT YOUR FRIEND SAID ABOUT YOU. ARE THEY SIMILAR OR DIFFERENT? IF NOT, WHY MIGHT THAT BE?

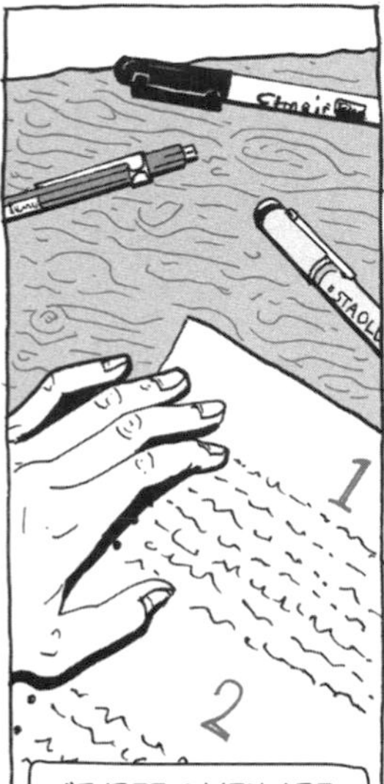
"THREE: WHEN ARE YOU AT YOUR BEST? THINK ABOUT WHAT YOU ENJOY OR WHERE YOUR STRENGTHS LIE. WHEN IN YOUR LIFE HAVE YOU FELT THIS WAY? FOR EXAMPLE, WORKING IN A TEAM, FIXING THINGS, DOING NUMBERS, BEING PRAISED. WHEN YOU'RE READY, WRITE IT DOWN.

"IT MAY HELP TO THINK ABOUT WHAT YOU WOULD NEVER DO. FOR EXAMPLE, YOU MIGHT NOT BE SUITED TO SITTING IN AN OFFICE ALL DAY, OR YOU MIGHT NOT SUPPORT WORKING FOR A TOBACCO COMPANY."

FINALLY!
NOW WE'RE JUST WAITING ON THOSE ZOO TICKETS...

THIS SPACE IS FOR YOUR REFLECTIONS | DATE: ....

WHAT ARE YOUR VALUES?

Write down some words that describe you. For example, kind, caring, ambitious.

THIS SPACE IS FOR YOUR REFLECTIONS | DATE: ....

WHAT VALUES WOULD OTHERS SAY YOU HAVE?

What values do you think others would say you have? You might want to ask your friends or family what their opinions are. This will give you insight.

THIS SPACE IS FOR YOUR REFLECTIONS | DATE: ....

HOW DO THESE TWO LISTS COMPARE?

Have a look at the list of words you wrote about yourself and then what you think others would say. Do you notice a difference?

THIS SPACE IS FOR YOUR REFLECTIONS | DATE: ....

WHEN ARE YOU AT YOUR BEST?

Write down what you are good at or enjoy doing, and in what environment. For example, I like working in a team that's supportive, or I like being out in nature.

don't go to the dark side lol

RECAP THREE

KNOW YOURSELF

- Your dreams are really important. You should listen to your heart.
- Your values tell you who you are. They give insight into how you'll make decisions towards your dreams.
- By knowing our values, we may present them to others and show the best of ourselves. Bring your natural passions to the surface.
- Learn and grow as you go, but take care to be kind and gentle with yourself.
- Some people may try to influence you, positively or negatively. You need to be aware of this and hold on to your dreams and values. Never sell out who you are. Appreciate this might take effort.

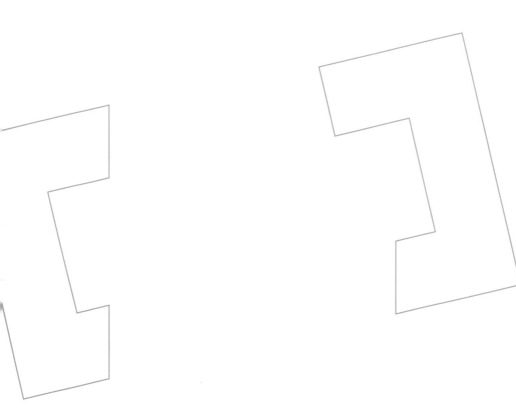

This space has been left for you.

ZAPIOS
dine in restaurant and bar

HEY, PRIYA. ARE YOU OK?
YEAH.

ARE YOU SURE? YOU LEFT THE PARTY EARLY AND YOU'VE NOT BEEN RETURNING MY TEXTS.
WELL I **WAS** PRETTY ILL, SOPHIE.

BUT, LIKE, YOU COULD'VE TOLD ME YOU WERE LEAVING.

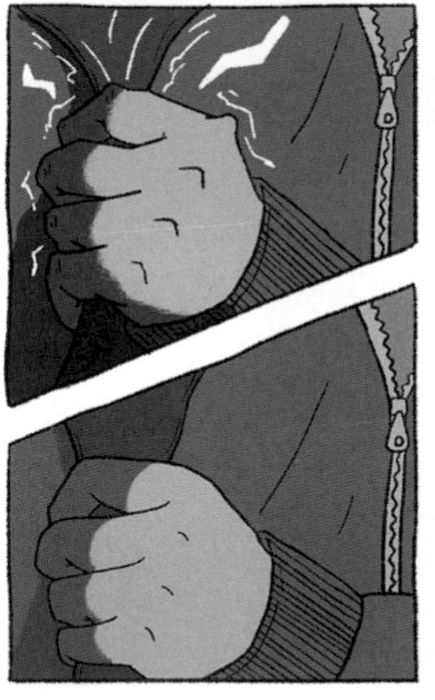

I'LL SEE YOU NEXT WEEK.
BYE.

PRIYA, WAIT!

WHAT'S GOING ON? ARE YOU MAD AT ME OR SOMETHING?
I DIDN'T EVEN DO ANYTHING WRONG!

WELL, GREAT. I GUESS EVERYTHING IS FINE, THEN!

HEY! PRIYA!
WAIT UP!

ARE YOU ALL RIGHT?

I CAN'T BELIEVE SHE JUST LEFT YOU THERE BY YOUR-SELF! SHE'S CLUELESS!
I KNOW. I WAS HONESTLY IN SUCH AS STATE AS WELL.
HER MATES JUST CHUCKED ME IN A TAXI, AND MY PARENTS WERE SO PISSED OFF! THEY SAID IF ANYTHING LIKE THIS HAPPENS AGAIN, I CAN'T DO THE COURSE ANYMORE.

I'M SO SORRY. I CAN'T BELIEVE SHE EVEN HANGS OUT WITH THESE PEOPLE.

I WOULDN'T HAVE MINDED SO MUCH IF I HADN'T BEEN SO ILL, AND IF THE TAXI HADN'T BEEN SO BLOODY EXPENSIVE.

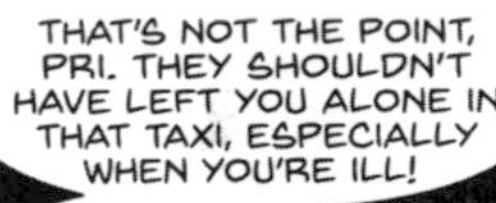
THAT'S NOT THE POINT, PRI. THEY SHOULDN'T HAVE LEFT YOU ALONE IN THAT TAXI, ESPECIALLY WHEN YOU'RE ILL!

AND SOPHIE SHOULDN'T HAVE LEFT YOU ALONE LIKE THAT WITH HER THOUGHT-LESS FRIENDS.

WHAT BOTHERS ME IS NOW SOPHIE JUST DOESN'T SEEM TO GET IT.
I KNOW. I'M SORRY YOU HAD TO GO THROUGH THIS. PLEASE PROMISE ME YOU'LL CALL IF SOMETHING LIKE THIS HAPPENS AGAIN.

THANKS, TASH. YOU'RE SO LOVELY.

IF I SAY YES TO THE ACCOUNTANTS, I CAN QUIT THIS SUPERMARKET JOB.

NO MORE RUDE CUSTOMERS OR THAT STUPID WEASEL THEY CALL A MANAGER.

NOT TO MENTION THEY'LL PAY ME MORE.

BUT THEN I WON'T HAVE ANY FREE TIME. NOT WITH EXAMS COMING UP.
HANG IN THERE

MOCK EXAM
LATE

HA! HA! HA! HA! HA! HA!

SO?*
*TRANSLATED FROM PASHTO.
THEY OFFERED ME THE JOB!

I KNEW IT! I COULD FEEL IT IN MY BONES!

YOU'D BETTER BE CAREFUL DANCING OR YOU'LL HAVE NO BONES LEFT!

WELL DONE, YASMIN.

I'M SO PROUD OF YOU.

I'M GOING TO MAKE SHEER YAKH, YOUR FAVOURITE, TO CELEBRATE!

YAY!

YOUR COOKING WILL BE THE DEATH OF ME.

PAP!

TO DIE TASTING SUCH SWEET HEAVEN AS YOUR COOKING. IT'S THE SECOND SWEETEST FEELING OF THE NIGHT.
WELL, SOMETHING HAD TO COME SECOND PLACE. IT'S NOT EVERY DAY OUR DAUGHTER BECOMES AN ACCOUNTANT!

YOUR MOTHER NEEDS LOTS OF REST. SHE HAS DEVELOPED CHRONIC STRESS LEADING TO EXHAUSTION.
I'D SUGGEST TAKING A FEW WEEKS OFF WORK, EVEN A LONG HOLIDAY.

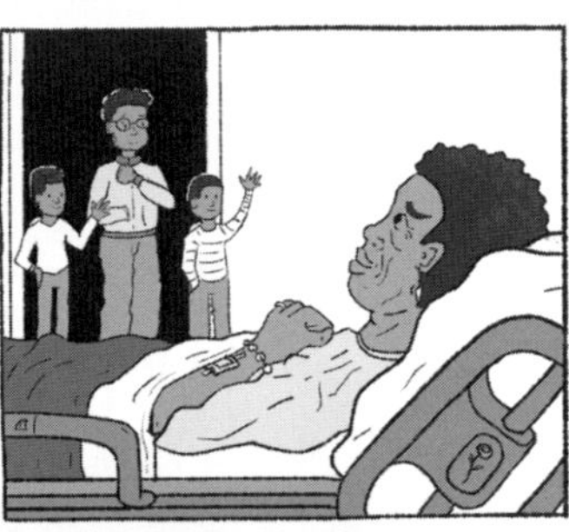

17:48
TJ
Hey TJ, could you come over and give me a hand this evening? 10:07am
I need your help with the project 10:07am
TJ
13:07pm
18:18

19:13

20:14
TJ
Hey Tj, could you come over and give me a hand this evening ? 10:07am
I need your help with the project 10:07am
TJ
13:07pm
Message

WHO'S TJ?

GET OUT!

YO, IT'S TJ! LEAVE A MESSAGE IF YOU'RE A DIV.

Click to add title

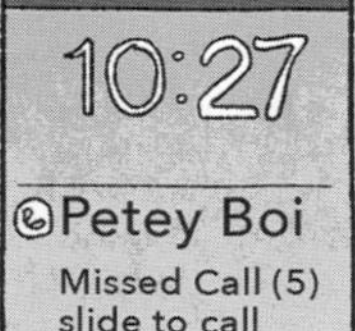
10:27
Petey Boi
Missed Call (5)
slide to call

SHIT...

Petey Boi
calling...
mute
add call

WHAT?

LISTEN, PETEY BOI. I'M SO SORRY I COMPLETELY FORGOT. I'M BARE WAVED. I DIDN'T EVEN CLOCK THE TIME.
IT'S FINE.

Beeeeeeeeep
Petey Boi
Call ended...
mute
keypad
add call
FaceTime

WHAT IS IT, TJ?
RING RING

BRO, I SAID I WAS SORRY, INNIT. SHIT HAPPENS. IT WAS JUST ONE MISTAKE MAN.

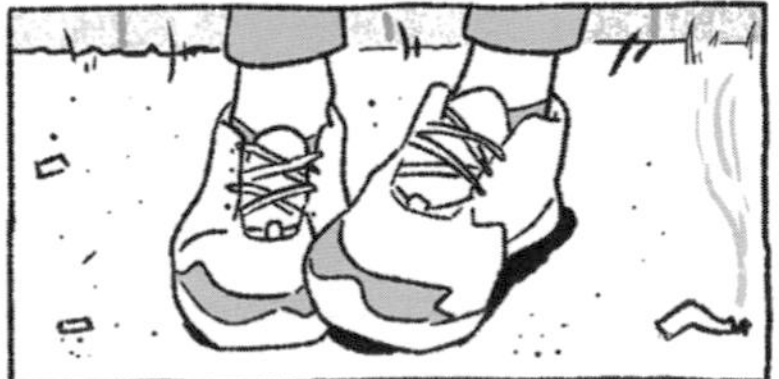

TJ, YOU OFFERED TO HELP.
I KNOW, BUT--
I REALLY DON'T HAVE TIME TO TALK RIGHT NOW.

JUST LEMME EXPLAIN FIRST...
AFTER WHAT HAPPENED THE OTHER NIGHT WITH THE, Y'KNOW... I MEAN...
I JUST, I DIDN'T KNOW WHERE WE STOOD, YOU AND ME. LIKE I DIDN'T THINK YOU'D EVEN WANT ME AROUND.
FORGET IT. YOU FOCUS ON YOUR SHIT, I'LL FOCUS ON MINE.
PETE--
THAT WAY EVERYONE'S HAPPY. DON'T WORRY, I WON'T ASK YOU TO HELP OUT AGAIN.
PETE--

TJ
02:31
END
FUCK!
SLAP!
BASH!!!
YO! TJ! GET BACK IN 'ERE! BAZ FOUND SOME FIT GIRLS.
FUCK IT.

BUZZ! BUZZ.

Incoming
Mum

HI, MUM.
NO, THEY'RE IN BED NOW.
DOCTOR SAYS YOU CAN BE OUT TOMORROW. I'LL COME PICK YOU UP ONCE I'VE DROPPED 'EM AT SCHOOL.

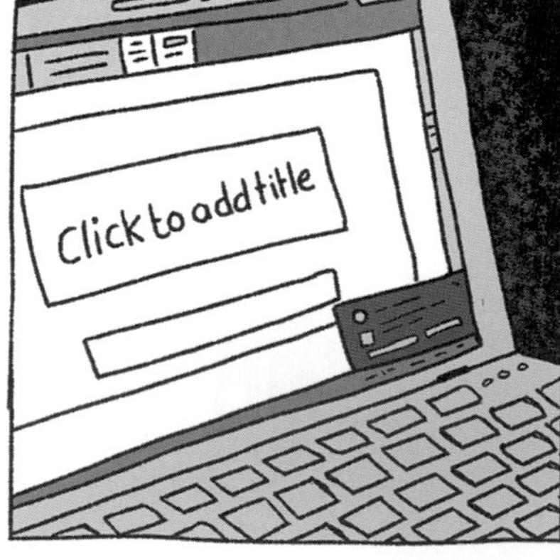
Click to add title

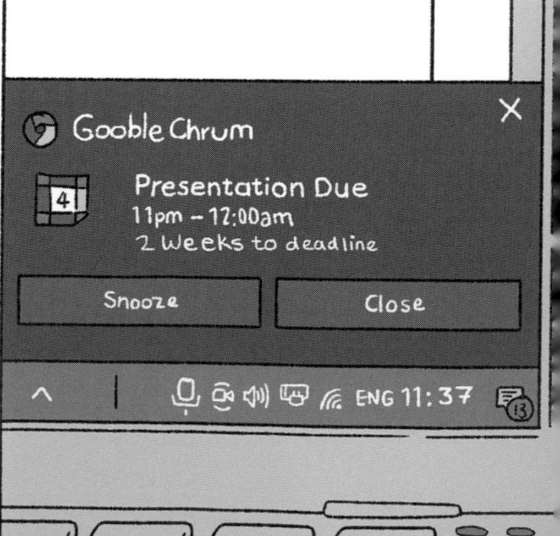
Gooble Chrum
4
Presentation Due
11pm – 12:00am
2 Weeks to deadline
Snooze
Close
ENG 11:37
13

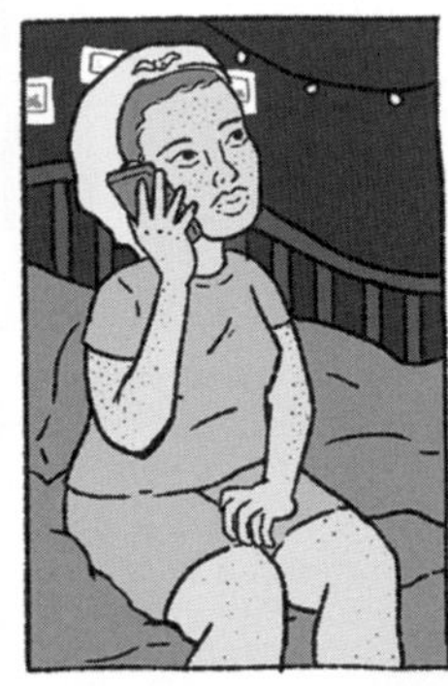

HEY.
Tash

HEY! WHAT'S UP?

NOTHING MUCH.
JUST WANTED TO SEE WHAT'S UP WITH YOU? YOU SEEMED A LITTLE UP-SET WHEN I LEFT THE GROUP.

YEAH!
I TRIED TALKING TO PRIYA BUT SHE SEEMED SUPER PISSED OFF FOR NO REASON!

I MEAN, SHE HAS A REASON.

EXCUSE ME?

YOU PUT HER IN A REALLY AWKWARD POSITION. SHE CAME OUT OF HER COMFORT ZONE TO SUPPORT YOU AND YOU DIDN'T EVEN SHOW UP.

I **DID** SHOW UP. **SHE** WAS THE ONE THAT LEFT ME ON MY OWN.

SHE WAS SICK! AND YOU LEFT HER ALONE IN THAT BIG POSH HOUSE WITH YOUR JUDGEMENTAL FRIENDS!

AND IF YOU CAN'T TELL THE DIFFERENCE BETWEEN **YOU** BEING LEFT ALONE AT THAT PARTY AND **PRIYA** BEING LEFT ALONE AT THAT PARTY...

...THEN I CAN'T HELP YOU.

WELL, THAT'S GREAT. BECAUSE I NEVER ASKED FOR YOUR HELP, TASH. SO WHY DON'T YOU STICK YOUR BIG NOSE IN SOME-ONE ELSE'S BUSINESS?!

HEY--

TASH SAYS YOU HAVE A PROBLEM WITH ME. I WANT TO HEAR IT FROM YOU.

YOU LEFT ME ALONE AT THAT PARTY... THE PROBLEM IS THAT YOU DON'T SEEM TO SEE ONE.
SO WHAT? MY FRIENDS SHOW UP LATE ON ME ALL THE TIME. WHAT'S THE BIG DEAL?

BECAUSE I'M NOT *YOU*, SOPHIE! AND NO OFFENCE BUT YOUR FRIENDS WEREN'T EXACTLY THE MOST WELCOMING CROWD!
THEY SENT ME HOME IN AN EXPENSIVE TAXI I COULDN'T AFFORD! WHILE I WAS REALLY ILL!
OH! AND ON TOP OF THAT, YOU WERE MAD AT *ME* FOR GOING HOME?!
I PUT MYSELF OUT THERE AND CAME ALL THAT WAY FOR YOU. YOU DIDN'T SHOW. THEN YOU GOT ANNOYED AT ME WHEN I GOT SICK. HOW THE HELL IS THAT FAIR?
SUMSANG
I... I UH, DIDN'T REALLY SEE IT THAT WAY...
WHY SHOULD YOU? LIVING THE LIFE YOU DO...
VOGE

WHAT'S THAT SUPPOSED TO MEAN?
Priya
IT MEANS WE CLEARLY DON'T HAVE TO WORRY ABOUT THE SAME THINGS.

SOME OF US JUST DON'T GET IT EASY.

PRIYA... I JUST...

NEXT TIME, CAN YOU JUST TELL ME WHEN I'VE DONE SOMETHING WRONG?

I THINK THAT'S SOME-THING YOU NEED TO FIGURE OUT FOR YOURSELF, SOPHIE.
SUMSANG

PRIYA...
Priya
Call ended

HEY HONEY. WHAT TIME AM I DROPPING YOU AT NATE'S? I THOUGHT THAT WAS IN A COUPLE OF MINUTES?

YEAH, UM... SORRY.

I'M NOT GOING...
...THEY CANCELLED.

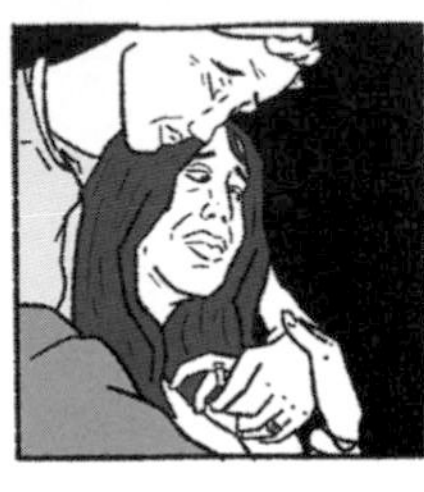

SMOOCH

WHY WOULD THEY WANT TO SEE ME?
WHY WOULD ANYONE WANT ME THERE?
LOOK AT YOU.
LOOK AT WHAT YOU LOOK LIKE...

CLICK
CLICK

OH NO. IT'S THOSE GIRLS.

HEY, ANDI!
HI, ANDI!

EPIC BUCKLE
SHIT SHIT SHIT SHIT...
SMACK!
ARE YOU ALL RIGHT?

ANDI.
IT'S YOUR TURN TO PRESENT.
COULD YOU PLEASE COME UP?

OK.
IT'S ALL RIGHT. JUST REMEMBER WHAT TASH SAID.
THEY'RE ALL JUST SHEEP. YOU'RE TALKING TO SHEEP.

BAAAH!

BAHHH

THAT WAS EASY...

THANK YOU, ANDI. WELL DONE. TAKE A SEAT, PLEASE.

I DON'T CARE IF IT WAS AN ACCIDENT!
SHE STILL THREW UP ON MY DAUGHTER'S UNIFORM.
HER ***EXPENSIVE*** UNIFORM, MIGHT I ADD!
AND IF THE SCHOOL WON'T PAY FOR IT, I WANT HER TO! I SHAN'T STAND FOR IT!

BARF!
CRINGE!

I HOPE YOU FEEL BETTER SOON, ANDI...

ANDI, COULD YOU PLEASE COME IN AND SHUT THE DOOR BEHIND YOU?

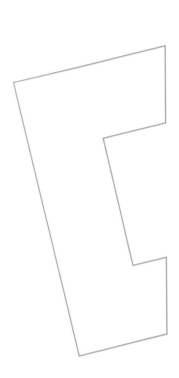

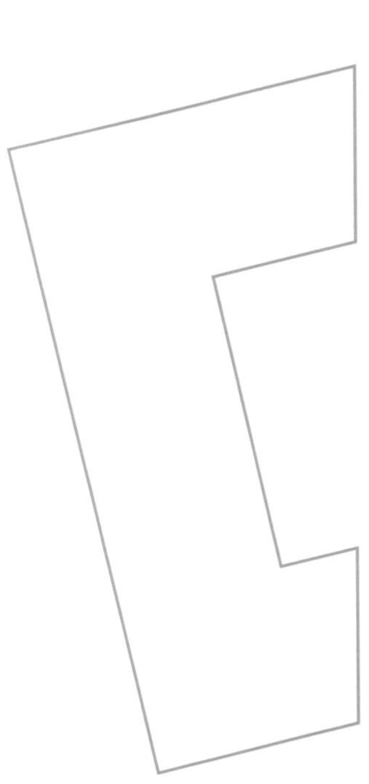

This space has been left for you.

STAGE FOUR

HELP YOURSELF

"INTELLIGENCE IS THE ABILITY TO ADAPT TO CHANGE." STEPHEN HAWKING*

*STEPHEN HAWKING WAS AN ENGLISH THEORETICAL PHYSICIST, COSMOLOGIST AND AUTHOR.

RIGHT, LET'S GET STARTED!
YES. PICKING UP WHERE WE LEFT OFF.
WE KNOW WHAT OUR DREAMS AND GOALS ARE. NOW IT'S TIME TO FIGURE OUT HOW WE GET THERE.

"JUST LIKE AN EXPLORER NEEDS TO READY THEM-SELVES FOR AN EXPEDITION, WE NEED TO PREPARE OUR-SELVES FOR OUR OWN ADVENTURE.

"MAKE SURE TO DO RESEARCH, AND PROPERLY CALCULATE THE RIGHT PATH FOR YOU BEFOREHAND.
!

TAH-DAH!
"TRY TO IDENTIFY HURDLES THAT MIGHT ARISE ON YOUR JOURNEY AND CONSIDER HOW YOU MIGHT OVERCOME THEM."

CROC AWAY SPRAY
Now effective in an 8 mile radius

SWING!

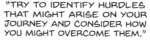

WHICH BIG BLOCKS CAN HELP YOU REACH YOUR DREAM?

BIG BLOCKS
OUR HEALTH IS THE FOUNDATION OF ALL OF THIS. LET'S LOOK AT AN EXAMPLE...
Goal 1
Talent 2
Talent 1
Start

Silent tap tap

I TRIPPED IN SCHOOL.

...OK, LET'S MOVE ON!

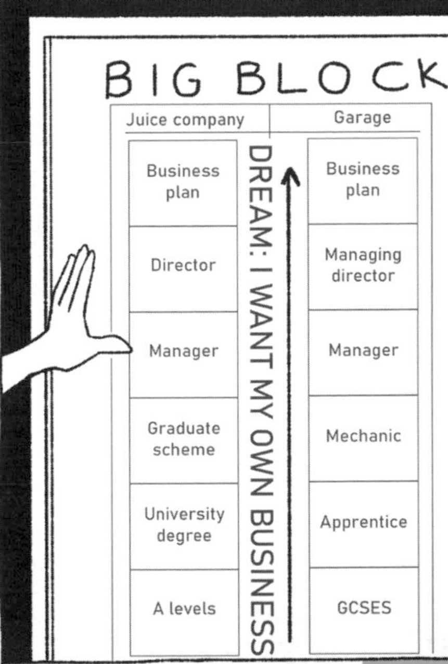

BIG BLOCKS
Juice company
Garage
HERE WE HAVE TWO BUSINESS CAREERS. EACH PERSON HAS TO PICK UP SKILLS IN ORDER TO CREATE THEIR OWN BUSINESS PLAN. BUT THERE ARE TWO WAYS OF BUILDING THOSE BLOCKS.
Business plan
Director
Manager
Graduate scheme
University degree
A levels
DREAM: I WANT MY OWN BUSINESS
Business plan
Managing director
Manager
Mechanic
Apprentice
GCSES

THEY BOTH WANTED THEIR OWN BUSINESS, AND THEY EACH USED THEIR SKILLS AND ACHIEVEMENTS AS INDIVIDUALS TO WORK THEIR WAY THERE.

BIG BLOCKS BUILD ON EACH OTHER

YOU CAN'T LOSE!

ARE A-LEVELS REALLY THAT IMPORTANT?

ANY EDUCATION OR TRAINING WE HAVE WILL ALWAYS HELP US. BUT TO ANSWER YOUR QUESTION, TJ, NO! THERE ARE SO MANY DIFFERENT ROUTES TO ACHIEVE YOUR GOALS AND BUILD YOUR KNOWLEDGE.

THESE BLOCKS ARE FOR YOU TO WORK WITH.
REMEMBER, THEY'RE SIMPLY GOALS, YOU DON'T HAVE TO HAVE THEM ALL UNDER YOUR BELT RIGHT NOW.

BLOCKS CAN BE STEPPING STONES TO YOUR DREAM

SO, THE BIG BLOCKS DEPEND ON WHAT OUR DREAM IS?
YEAH, PRETTY MUCH. I FOUND IT'S EASIER TO START BACKWARDS.

RIGHT...

MY DREAM IS TO BE... A NINJA WARRIOR.
HOW DO I GO BACKWARDS FROM THERE?
MOONWALK?

He He He He He

WE KNOW IDENTIFYING THE BIG BLOCKS GIVES US CLUES ON WHERE TO START LOOKING.
BUT IF WE DON'T KNOW HOW TO START TRACING A PATH, DOING YOUR OWN RESEARCH IS VERY HELPFUL.
Scribble
Scribble
Scribble
Scribble

USING THE INTERNET OR EVEN YOUR SAFARI SKILLS.
ASK AROUND. YOU'LL FIND SO MANY PEOPLE USE ALL DIFFERENT KINDS OF BLOCKS TO GET TO THE SAME PLACE.

EXPLORING DIFFERENCES ENHANCES PERSONAL DISCOVERY

THINK BEYOND

THE BLOCK AHEAD

KEEP YOUR HEAD UP

WE'RE GOING TO CONTINUE TALKING ABOUT BIG BLOCKS.
I WANT YOU TO THINK ABOUT HOW THE BLOCK AHEAD GETS YOU TO THE BLOCK BEYOND.
DON'T JUST THINK OF WHAT'S IMMEDIATELY IN FRONT OF YOU.
WHY DO YOU THINK WE SHOULD TRY TO THINK BEYOND THE BLOCK AHEAD?

IT'S USEFUL TO THINK ABOUT WHEN EVALUATING OPPORTUNITIES THAT COME UP.

YEAH MAN. I GUESS WE CAN APPLY THIS TO ANYTHING WE DO.

IT HELPS US STAY ON COURSE.

SO THAT IF WE WERE LOOKING FOR A JOB, WE THINK ABOUT HOW IT WILL GET US TO THE NEXT JOB?

SOPHIE, PRIYA, WHAT DO YOU TWO THINK?

TASH. COULD YOU PUT YOUR PHONE AWAY PLEASE?
TIP
Tap
TIP

SORRY, JEN...

REMEMBER, WHAT MIGHT SEEM IMPOSSIBLE

CAN BE ACHIEVED

I'LL TELL YOU A STORY TO BRING THIS TO LIFE. HAVE YOU HEARD OF JAMAL EDWARDS?

YEAH!
SADLY, HE PASSED AWAY YOUNG, BUT HIS STORY IS INSPIRING. HE LOVED MUSIC. HE WAS VERY DRIVEN BUT DIDN'T LEAVE SCHOOL WITH THE QUALIFICATIONS HE WANTED. BUT HE STILL HAD A DREAM.

CLUB
Luna
SECURITY
EXIT ONLY
"SO HE BEGAN JOURNEYING INTO MUSIC HIS OWN WAY. HE DECIDED TO TALK TO GRIME STARS, WAITING OUTSIDE NIGHTCLUBS TO INTERVIEW THEM, WHICH OFTEN WORKED. HE WAS THE ONLY ONE DOING THIS."

HAVE A GO

DON'T BE AFRAID OF REJECTION, IT'S ESSENTIAL TO PROGRESS

WHAT'S THE WORST THAT CAN HAPPEN?

"GRIME WAS AN EMERGING MUSIC GENRE AS HE WAS AN EMERGING JOURNALIST. HE WORKED HARD, FILMING MUSIC VIDEOS, AND SPEAKING WITH COUNTLESS CELEBRITIES.
"OVER TIME, HE BUILT UP A LOT OF CONTENT. HE BECAME KNOWN AS AN EXPERT. EACH INTERVIEW HE DID WAS A BLOCK TOWARDS OPENING DOORS FOR HIMSELF AND OTHERS.
0:27 / 2:35
SB.TV - 100K Subscribers - Jamal Edwards (SB)
36,225 views Sep 7, 2011 Jamal Edwards AKA SB has a few words of sincere gratification to share in light of reaching 100,000 subscriber ...more
SBTV: Music
1.23M subscribers
SUBSCRIBE

"EVENTUALLY, HE SET UP HIS OWN TV CHANNEL CALLED SBTV. IT EXPANDED INTO OTHER MUSIC STYLES AND IS NOW WORTH MILLIONS. HE WAS ONE OF THE MOST INFLUENTIAL PEOPLE IN MUSIC, HE WAS EVEN AWARDED AN MBE BY QUEEN ELIZABETH II!
"BUT HE STARTED WITH THAT VERY FIRST BLOCK, GOING OUT AND MEETING PEOPLE IN A WAY THAT NO ONE ELSE WAS."

SO, HOW DO YOU THINK YOU CAN GET TO YOUR FIRST BLOCK?

PEOPLE CAN HELP YOU

GET TO BLOCK 1 AND BEYOND

WHY NOT EXPLORE?

THINK ABOUT PEOPLE, PLACES OR PRODUCTS THAT MIGHT HELP

WHAT BLOCKS CAN HELP YOU ACHIEVE YOUR DREAMS?

Think of the steps, or building blocks, you need to get through in order to achieve your end goal. It might help to start with your dream and work backwards.

THIS SPACE IS FOR YOUR REFLECTIONS | DATE: ....

PEOPLE: WHO COULD HELP YOU ON YOUR JOURNEY?

Think about people you know, or might have connections to the type of work you're interested in. Think of ways you might be able to make connections yourself.

THIS SPACE IS FOR YOUR REFLECTIONS | DATE: ....

PLACES: WHERE DO YOU NEED TO RESEARCH OR VISIT?

To get a good feel of what it's like to work in an area you're interested in, it's a great idea to research the culture or visit. Don't be afraid to ask!

THIS SPACE IS FOR YOUR REFLECTIONS | DATE: ....

PRODUCTS: WHAT THINGS MIGHT YOU NEED TO HELP YOU?

This could be anything from pens, paper, art supplies, books, computer equipment, access to the internet for research or online courses. Think about getting equipped!

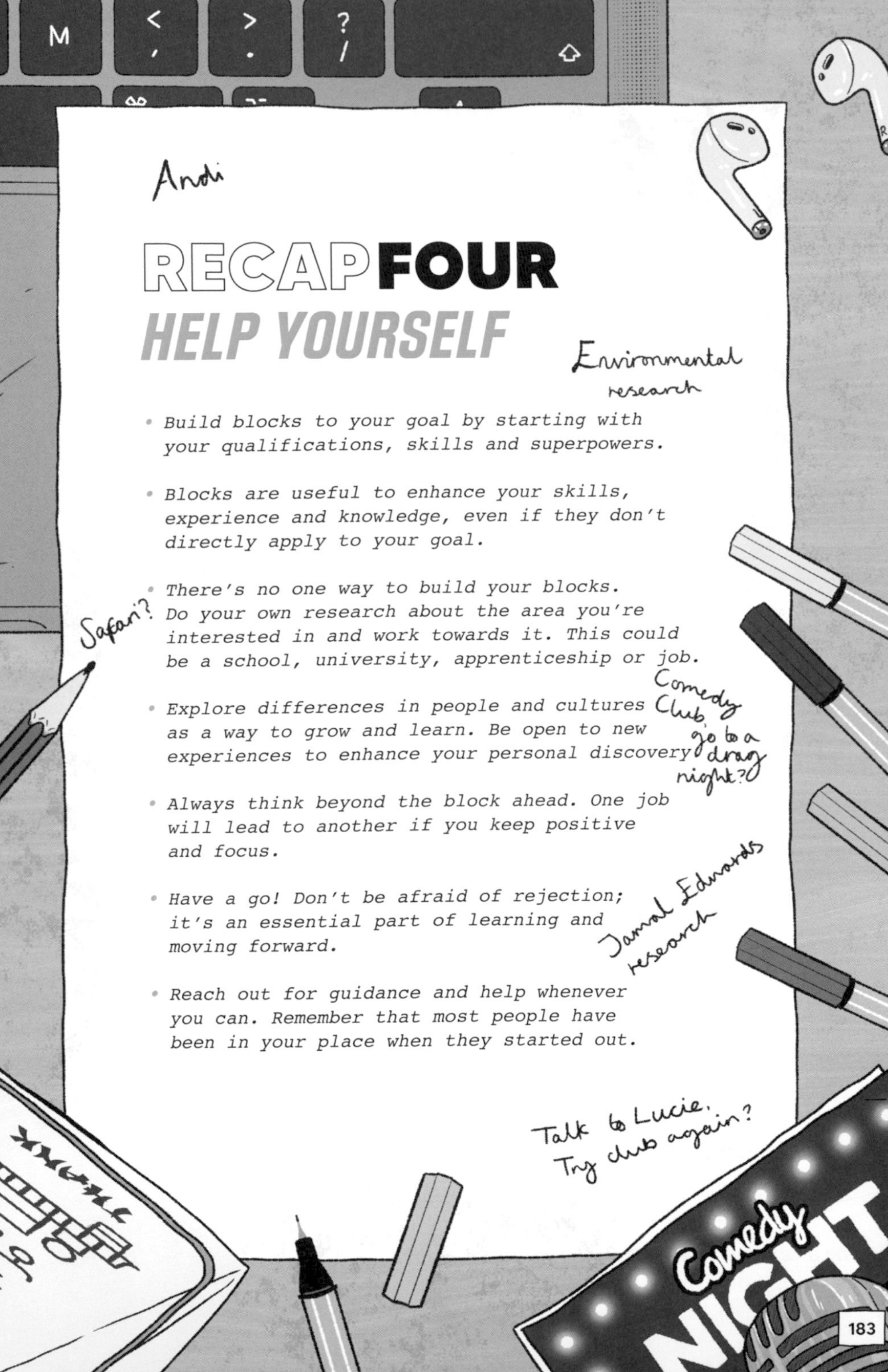

RECAP FOUR

HELP YOURSELF

- Build blocks to your goal by starting with your qualifications, skills and superpowers.
- Blocks are useful to enhance your skills, experience and knowledge, even if they don't directly apply to your goal.
- There's no one way to build your blocks. Do your own research about the area you're interested in and work towards it. This could be a school, university, apprenticeship or job.
- Explore differences in people and cultures as a way to grow and learn. Be open to new experiences to enhance your personal discovery.
- Always think beyond the block ahead. One job will lead to another if you keep positive and focus.
- Have a go! Don't be afraid of rejection; it's an essential part of learning and moving forward.
- Reach out for guidance and help whenever you can. Remember that most people have been in your place when they started out.

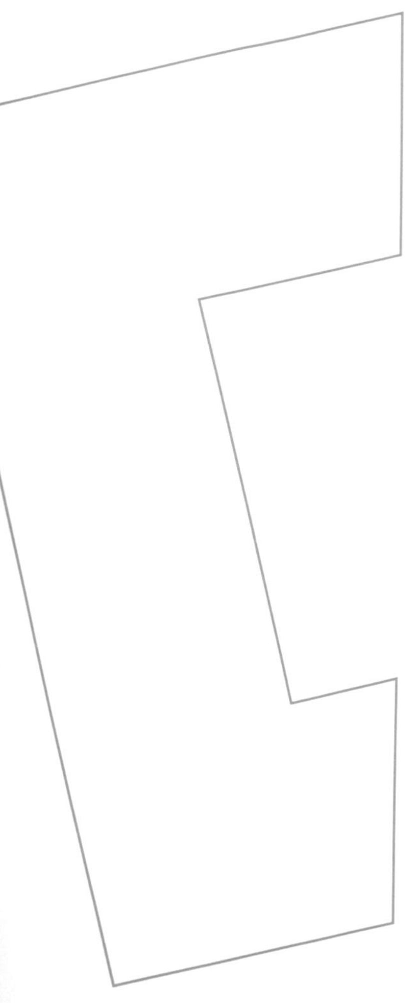

This space has been left for you.

TASH! COULD I GRAB YOU FOR A MOMENT?

I'VE NOTICED HOW MUCH YOU LOOK AT YOUR PHONE AND I'M GETTING A LITTLE CONCERNED, TASH.
WHAT DO YOU MEAN BY "CONCERNED?"

OK, WHY?
HOW MANY HOURS DO YOU SPEND ON THAT THING?
I DON'T KNOW... A LOT I SUPPOSE.

IT'S A PHONE...
EXACTLY. IT'S JUST A PHONE. BUT I FEEL LIKE IT'S MORE THAN THAT TO YOU. IT WORRIES ME.

SORRY NEERA. I'LL TURN IT OFF FOR THE LESSONS.

HAVE YOU EVER THOUGHT ABOUT TRYING TO TURN IT OFF FOR A FULL DAY?
BUT WHAT IF SOMEONE NEEDS ME? LIKE IT'S AN EMERGENCY OR SOME-THING?

OK, TRY IT WHEN YOU'RE AT HOME, IN YOUR DOWNTIME. WHEN THERE'S NO ONE THAT NEEDS YOU ON SPEED DIAL.
BUT WHAT ABOUT MY FOLLOWERS?

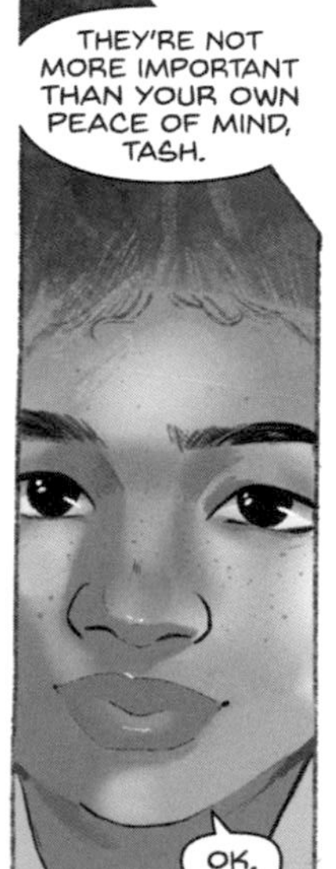
THEY'RE NOT MORE IMPORTANT THAN YOUR OWN PEACE OF MIND, TASH.
OK.

10:21
NEW MESSAGE
hey soph, sorry I missed these messages, it was a mad week! why weren't you at tommos yesterday?! OMG so much happened xx
Hey Bea, actually been having a pretty rough time recently, feeling really down... maybe we could go for a coffee later?xxx

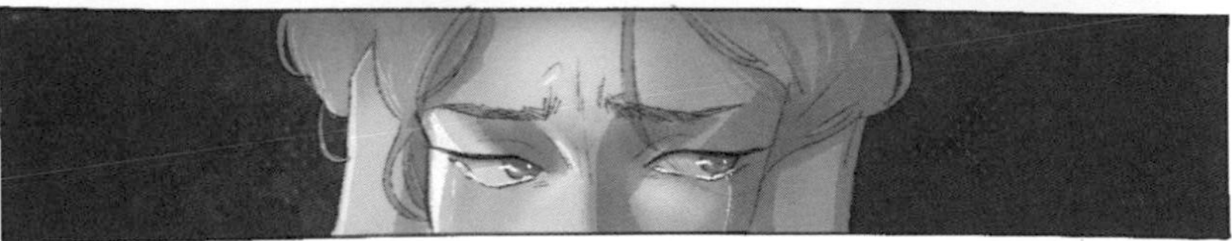
oh sorry to hear it babes, I'm sure you'll feel better soon! go get some ice cream, that's what always helps me lol. but yeah can't do today, how's the weekend? anyway so yh the drama, tommo totes slept with kelly and then ems like literally walked in on them! was so bait xx

PLEASE PICK UP
PLEASE PICK UP
RING RING RING RING RING RING
HELLO?
HEY, PRIYA...
HEY, SOPHIE...
CAN WE TALK?
ABOUT WHAT HAPPENED?

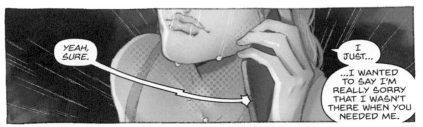

YEAH, SURE.
I JUST...
...I WANTED TO SAY I'M REALLY SORRY THAT I WASN'T THERE WHEN YOU NEEDED ME.

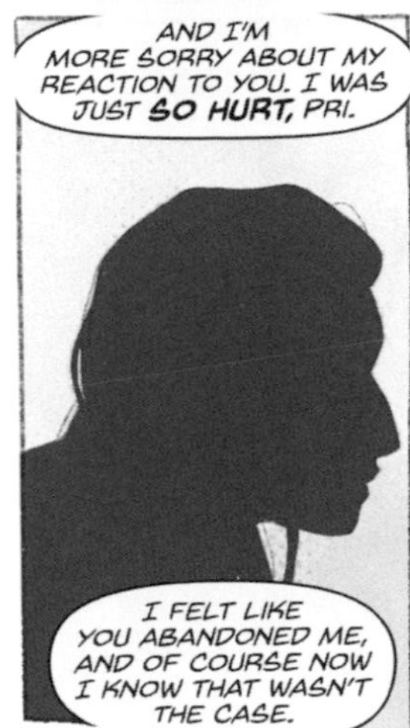

AND I'M MORE SORRY ABOUT MY REACTION TO YOU. I WAS JUST **SO HURT,** PRI.
I FELT LIKE YOU ABANDONED ME, AND OF COURSE NOW I KNOW THAT WASN'T THE CASE.

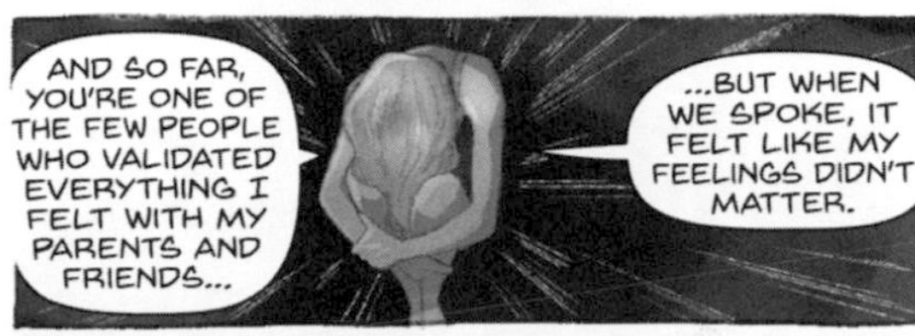

AND SO FAR, YOU'RE ONE OF THE FEW PEOPLE WHO VALIDATED EVERYTHING I FELT WITH MY PARENTS AND FRIENDS...
...BUT WHEN WE SPOKE, IT FELT LIKE MY FEELINGS DIDN'T MATTER.

I'M SORRY TOO, SOPH.
LOOK, I WON'T LIE, YOU REALLY UPSET ME. BUT I THINK YOUR FRIENDS UPSET ME MORE.

IF YOU'RE DEALING WITH THEM ALL THE TIME, THEN I CAN UNDERSTAND YOUR REACTION.

I TOTALLY SEE HOW THEIR ATTITUDE TO FRIENDSHIP WOULD BREAK A PERSON DOWN. YOU DON'T DESERVE THAT.
FRIENDS, YEAH?

YES PLEASE.
I'LL SEE YOU NEXT WEEK AT [RE]START.
I'LL SEE YOU THERE.

BZZZZZ

Hey Bea, do you reckon I could bring a plus one to Steph's 2morro?xx
Yh sure. Is it a boy? What's his name?- cause I can totally wing woman you?xx
It's my friend Priya, from the party. xx
Oh, I just checked in and I think numbers are pretty tight actually. Maybe next time though k? xx

MAYBE NOT...

...AND THIS LAST ONE HERE IS FROM AUNT DEBBIE.
SPEEDY RECOVERY
AWH, HOW SWEET. HAVEN'T SEEN HER FOR A FEW YEARS...

...PETER DEAREST, IT'S GETTING LATE. COULD YOU GET SOME FOOD FOR THE BOYS?

TAP TAP
SURE, MUM.

THUD!!
Sigh

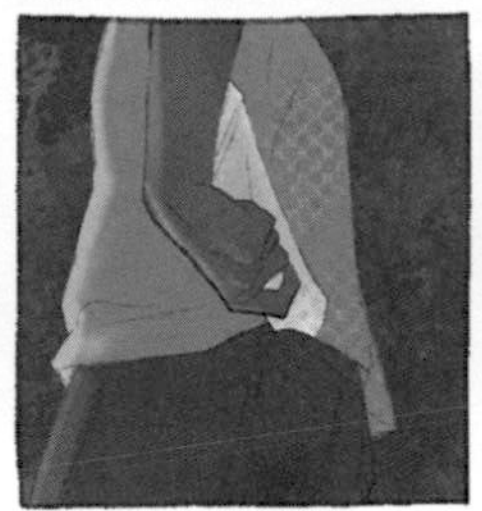

LATE RENT NOTICE
GREAT.

EMPTY
PETE! ISAAC IS CHEATING!
EXTRA GREAT.
AM NOT!
LUKE'S KICKING ME!
PETE!

I NEED TO HEAD TO THE SHOP REAL QUICK, OK? LOOK AFTER MUM.
AND PLEASE...
...STOP FIGHTING.
NICE. GOOD TALK...
...UH, SORRY, THIS SHOULD BE WORKING!
I SWEAR THERE WAS SOME MONEY LEFT ON HERE...
DECLINED
I'M REALLY SORRY, SIR, BUT I'M GOING TO HAVE TO ASK YOU TO MOVE ALONG.

FUCK.
STUPID...
...CARD...
...STUPID MONEY...
...STUPID...
...ANXIETY...
...IT'S OK... BREATHE SLOWLY...
SHIT.
OK, WHAT NOW...?
RING RING RING
HEY, MO SORRY TO CALL UNANNOUNCED. I'M ACTUALLY NOT DOING TOO GREAT.
I COULD DO WITH SOME WISE WORDS IF YOU'VE GOT A MINUTE?
YOU'VE COME TO THE RIGHT PLACE. HOW CAN I HELP YOU, PETE?
THERE'S JUST SO MUCH GOING ON RIGHT NOW...
...MY MUM'S ILL, SO I'M LOOKING AFTER MY BROTHERS.
I HAVE NO TIME FOR MY INTERNSHIP WHICH I REALLY WANT TO DO...
...BUT I DON'T KNOW IF I SHOULD. WE NEED MONEY AND MUM CAN'T WORK.
SO MAYBE I SHOULD GET A REAL JOB, BUT I DON'T HAVE TIME TO APPLY...
...BECAUSE I WANT TO DO THE COURSE!

I JUST... JUST...
HEY! HEY, IT'S OK. WE'LL FIGURE THIS OUT.
...I JUST FEEL SO OVERWHELMED. STUCK. LIKE MY DREAMS ARE RIGHT THERE TO GRAB BUT MY HANDS ARE TIED BEHIND ME...
...WE ALWAYS TALK ABOUT VALUES ON THE COURSE...
...BUT I CAN'T SEE HOW I CAN HONOUR MY OWN AMBITIONS AND ALSO HONOUR HOW I VALUE THOSE I CARE FOR.
FIRSTLY, WELL DONE FOR REACHING OUT FOR HELP. I KNOW IT'S TERRIFYING TO DO, BUT SO EXTREMELY IMPORTANT.
IT SOUNDS LIKE THE ISSUE IS YOU'VE NO SPACE FOR YOURSELF RIGHT NOW?
BASICALLY...

SO LET'S ASK FOR MORE HELP. IS THERE ANYONE WHO CAN HELP OUT WITH YOUR HOME SITUATION? FAMILY OR FRIENDS?

ERM, I SUPPOSE I COULD ASK MY AUNT.
SHE DOESN'T TALK TO MY MUM MUCH, BUT...
...SHE'S ALWAYS BEEN THERE WHEN NEEDED BEFORE.

OK, SOUNDS GOOD. NEXT IS THE INTERNSHIP.
I SUGGEST YOU WRITE TO THEM.

TELL THEM THAT YOU'RE LOOKING AFTER YOUR SICK MOTHER AND YOUNGER BROTHERS TEMPORARILY.

ASK FOR AN EXTENSION.
WON'T THEY THINK I'M MAKING AN EXCUSE?
WELL, YOU ARE GIVING A REASON, NOT MAKING AN EXCUSE.

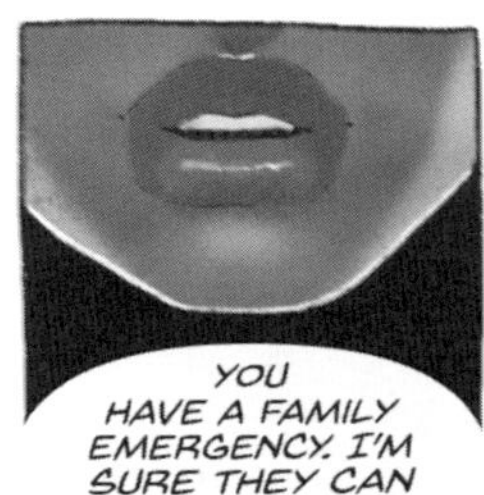

YOU HAVE A FAMILY EMERGENCY. I'M SURE THEY CAN SHOW SOME EMPATHY OR LENIENCY IN SCHEDULING YOUR INTERVIEW.

IF THEY DON'T HELP, PERHAPS IT'S NOT A GREAT PLACE TO WORK.

I... I GUESS SO.
THANKS, MO. I APPRECIATE THIS.

ARE YOU SURE YOU'RE FEELING BETTER? YOU KNOW A CONCUSSION CAN BE SERIOUS.*
I PROMISE I'M FINE, BABA.
IF I WASN'T, THE SCHOOL NURSE WOULDN'T LET ME GO.
WELL, IF YOU GET ANY ODD HEADACHES OR THAT GIRL'S MOTHER GIVES YOU ANY MORE TROUBLE, YOU MAKE SURE TO LET US KNOW.

*TRANSLATED FROM CANTONESE.

...
ANDI...?
IS EVERYTHING OK?
I... I JUST DON'T KNOW IF IT WAS A GREAT IDEA TO COME HERE.

WHAT DO YOU MEAN, DEAR?
MAYBE IT'S THE LANGUAGE BARRIER OR SOMETHING? BUT I'M JUST HAVING A REALLY HARD TIME FITTING IN.
EVERYTHING I DO SEEMS TO GO WRONG AND I DON'T KNOW IF I CAN KEEP UP.
SWEETHEART, WE ARE SO PROUD OF YOU FOR DOING THIS. PUTTING YOURSELF OUT THERE IS HARD ENOUGH...
...LET ALONE IN A DIFFERENT COUNTRY!

EXACTLY, STOP PUTTING SO MUCH PRESSURE ON YOURSELF TO MAKE THINGS RIGHT.
Mama and Baba
27:19
YOU'RE YOUNG. YOU'RE ALLOWED TO MAKE MISTAKES. ESPECIALLY WHEN YOU'RE JUST FIGURING OUT WHO YOU ARE!

THANKS...
...I REALLY MISS YOU BOTH.

AND WHERE BETTER TO MESS UP THAN HALFWAY ACROSS THE WORLD WHERE YOU CAN JUST LEAV--
SHE DOESN'T NEED TO HEAR THAT!
WHAT?! BUT IT'S TRUE!
I LOVE YOU BOTH.
WE LOVE YOU TOO...

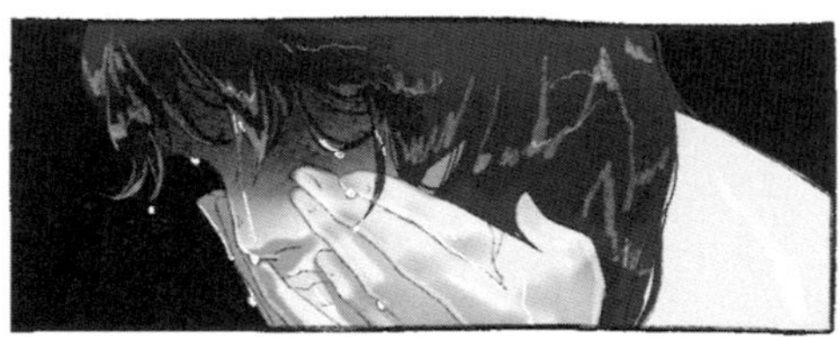

YOU GOT THIS...

OI, WHERE'S THE PORK?
THOUGH I DON'T SUPPOSE YOU'D KNOW WHAT PORK LOOKS LIKE, EH?
OF COURSE! IT'S DOWN IN AISLE FIVE TO THE LEF--
ARE YOU SURE?
JUST YOU DON'T SOUND LIKE YOU KNOW ENGLISH VERY WELL. DON'T WANT TO WASTE MY TIME.
URM... EXCUSE ME?
LET'S FIND SOMEONE ELSE, PRETTY SURE HER KIND DON'T EVEN EAT MEAT ANYWAY...
DON'T STARE, STACY, MUMMY TOLD YA BEFORE... IT'S RUDE.
REC 15:53:37
...SO YEAH, JUST FILL OUT THESE FORMS AND WE'LL SEND THEM UP TO HEAD OFFICE.

WHAT WILL HAPPEN THEN?
I DON'T KNOW. LIKE, THEY MIGHT COME INTERVIEW YOU FOR THE RECORDS, OR SOMETHING. THEN, LIKE YEAH...

...THAT'S ABOUT IT.
HAVE YOU EVER THOUGHT ABOUT TAKING IT OFF?
EXCUSE ME? TAKE ***WHAT*** OFF?

eye-roll
YOUR HEAD SCARF. OBVIOUSLY, LIKE, JUST FOR WORK HOURS.

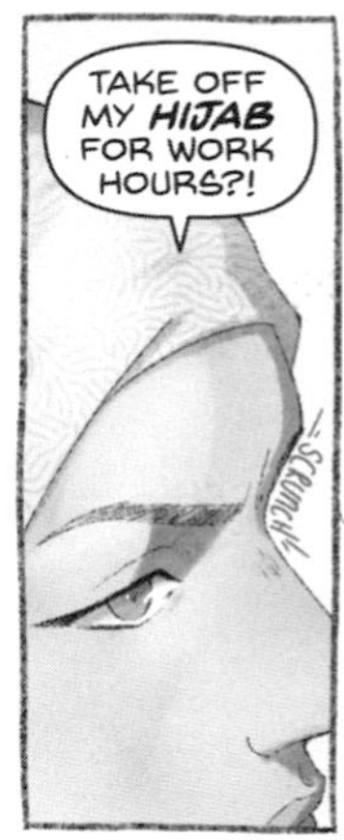
TAKE OFF MY ***HIJAB*** FOR WORK HOURS?!
scrunch

Y'KNOW, LIKE, WE'RE IN A PRETTY BAD AREA FOR THAT SORT OF STUFF SO, LIKE, WEARING IT IS KINDA ASKING FOR IT.
HEY, LOOK, IT'S JUST A SUGGESTION!
I'M NOT SAYING YOU HAVE TO, OF COURSE, JUST BRAIN-STORMING.

LIKE, I'M JUST SAYING. THEY WON'T BE ABLE TO PICK YOU OUT THAT WAY, IS ALL.

WELL. ***I*** SUGGEST ***YOU*** START HIRING NEW STAFF, BECAUSE ***I QUIT.***

CLICK
GEEZ.
SO DAMN SENSITIVE...

YASMIN, HONEY? IS THAT YOU?*
HEY, MOR! YEAH, IT'S ME!
*TRANSLATED FROM PASHTO.
YOU'RE HOME EARLY. I THOUGHT YOU FINISHED AT SEVEN?
YEAH, ALL GOOD! JUST FELT A BIT ILL SO THEY LET ME OFF EARLY.
OH DEAR! HOLD ON I'LL BRING YOU A HOT DRINK.
NO! IT'S OK, THANKS, I MEAN...
...JUST GONNA GET SOME SLEEP, THANKS. LOVE YOU.
OK. LOVE YOU, MASHOOMA. I'LL COME UP IN A SHORT WHILE TO WAKE YOU.

So... I just feel like I'm hiding something and I just can't anymore. I just wanna lay it all out. I feel like everyone who knows me thinks I'm this super happy and easy going girl but in reality I hate mys|

Edit

easy going girl but in reality I'm so lost and unhappy and feel so inadequate. My friends will soon all leave me behind and I'm just pretending that they won't. I know it isn't their fault and I'm happy for ther just don't know how to finc

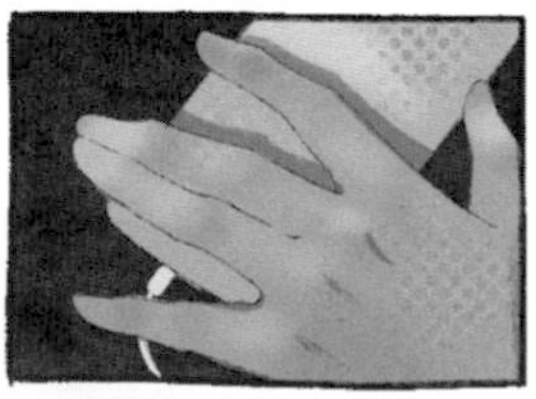
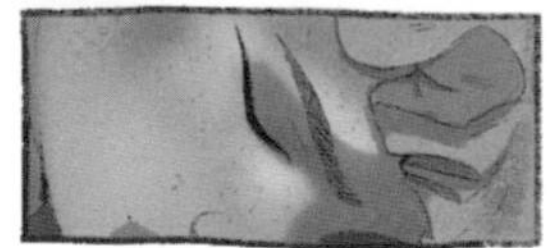

OH MY GOD
OH MY GOD
NO NO NO NO NO
NO NO NO NO NO
for real?! Gimmie a ca
Claire
Hey r we gud? Jus kinda..
Callum
Babe!!! pls tell me you're..
Mama #1
Hello love, we're having..
Mommy #A
Save me fr your Mom..
Gram
jus.tin.1 commented: "thi
problem with society
Everyone thi
in a long while lol
Queen <3
an pls shut your privilaged slu
OH MY GOD.
GODDAMMIT, TASH.
FUCKING STUPID!
AGGHHHHH
Requests
messages • 7h

ARE YOU SURE WE CAN'T GET YOU ANYTHING?

YEAH MOM...

...I'M GOOD.

ACTUALLY, I DON'T FEEL GREAT. DO YOU MIND IF I MISS THE BBQ?

OK, DEAR...

...ARE YOU SURE? WE CAN STAY BEHIND!

I THINK THERE'S A NEW EPISODE OF SELLING SUNRISE.

I'D PREFER THAT TO SHIRLEY'S POTATO SALAD!

NO, NO. PLEASE GO. ENJOY YOURSELVES.

RING RING ring RING ring RING

CALLING YAZ

RING RING ring RING

HEY, YASMIN?

HEY, TASH. WHAT'S UP?

OH, URM, NOTHING MUCH. JUST... WONDERING HOW YOU'RE DOING.
HOW'S THE NEW ACCOUNTANCY JOB AND THE GOOD OL' SUPERMARKET?

I, UH, ACTUALLY QUIT WORK TODAY.

OH, SHIT, REALLY?! HOW COME?

JUST HAD A STUPID WOMAN AND HER DAUGHTER INSULT ME BECAUSE OF MY HIJAB.

THEN MY MANAGER ***SUGGESTED*** I SIMPLY TAKE IT OFF AT WORK.

OH MY GOD. I'M SO SORRY YASMIN.

THING IS, IT'S NOT LIKE THIS IS THE FIRST TIME. WHEN-EVER IT HAPPENS, I START TO DOUBT MYSELF.

LIKE HOW I SPEAK ENGLISH, HOW I LOOK...
...MAYBE I SHOULD JUST TAKE THIS ACCOUNTANCY JOB AND GET OUT OF HERE.

I'M SO SORRY. YOU SHOULDN'T HAVE TO DEAL WITH THAT.
I CAN'T BELIEVE PEOPLE LIKE THAT EVEN EXIST.

BUT THEY'RE THE ONES WHO SHOULD FEEL SHIT. NOT YOU, YASMIN.

YOU'RE GOING PLACES. YOU'RE BRIGHT AND PRETTY AND SUPER NICE.
THANKS, TASH...
...YOU'RE SO LOVELY.

I MEAN, YOU'VE ALREADY GOT A FANCY NEW JOB ANY-WAY!
I KNOW. EXCEPT... I KINDA HATE ACCOUNTING...

OH.
...AND I KINDA HAVEN'T TOLD MY PARENTS, WHO ARE SUPER PROUD...

LOOK. YOU'VE GOT TO FOLLOW YOUR HEART WITH THIS JOB, YASMIN.

IF YOU DON'T FEEL IT, YOU WON'T BE HAPPY. AND THAT'S ALL YOUR PARENTS WANT FOR YOU, RIGHT?
BUT WHAT IF I CAN'T GET ANYTHING ELSE?

YAS, THEY OFFERED YOU AN APPRENTICE-SHIP YOU DIDN'T EVEN **WANT!**

JUST IMAGINE WHAT COULD HAPPEN WHEN YOU TRY FOR SOMETHING YOU **REALLY** WANT!
THANKS, TASH. Y'KNOW, YOU'RE REALLY SMART.

I WISH I COULD SEE THINGS THE WAY YOU DO. IT'S A REAL TALENT.
HEH... THANKS. IT'S GOOD TO KNOW I'M DOING **SOMETHING** RIGHT...

WHAT DO YOU MEAN? ARE YOU FEELING ALL RIGHT?
OH, NO NO. DON'T WORRY. YOU HAVE ENOUGH ON YOUR PLATE YASMIN--
TASH, PLEASE. I'M YOUR FRIEND, I WANT TO BE HERE FOR YOU.
I... I THINK I HAVE A PROBLEM.
I'VE JUST BEEN FEELING... LOW RECENTLY.

I MADE AN INSTA POST ABOUT IT. NOW I THINK ALL MY FRIENDS HATE ME FOR WHAT I SAID.
*I DON'T THINK ANYONE COULD **HATE** YOU, TASH. HAVE YOU SPOKEN TO THEM ABOUT IT?*

I CAN'T... I DON'T WANT TO HEAR HOW MUCH I'VE DISAPPOINTED THEM.
I THINK MAYBE YOU NEED TO CUT YOURSELF SOME SLACK.
HUH?

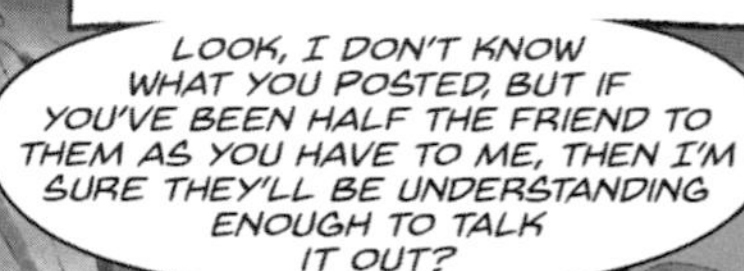
LOOK, I DON'T KNOW WHAT YOU POSTED, BUT IF YOU'VE BEEN HALF THE FRIEND TO THEM AS YOU HAVE TO ME, THEN I'M SURE THEY'LL BE UNDERSTANDING ENOUGH TO TALK IT OUT?

THE IMPORTANT THING TO REMEMBER IS YOU'RE THE ONE HURTING HERE, NOT THEM. IF THEY CHOOSE TO CUT YOU OFF FOR THAT INSTEAD OF HELPING YOU UP BACK UP ON YOUR FEET THEN THAT'S ON THEM.

FRIENDS HELP FRIENDS, ESPECIALLY WHEN THEY'RE FEELING DOWN, RIGHT?
I GUESS.

WHY NOT GIVE IT A TRY?
JUST REACH OUT TO ONE OF THEM AND TELL THEM THE TRUTH ABOUT HOW YOU'RE FEELING.

COME *OONNN,* BRUV.
DON'T BE A WASTEMAN. IT'S GONNA BE LIT.
I'VE GOT STUFF TO DO, ALL RIGHT?
IMPORTANT STUFF.
BRO. STOP FUCKING ABOUT.
WE'RE YOUR BOYS. YOU CAN'T DITCH US.

?
LOOK. NO DISRESPECT.
BUT I GOTTA STAY IN AND GET ON TOP OF MY SHIT.

SLAM

C'MON, *"BRUV."*
YOUR MATES ARE A BIT THICK, AREN'T THEY?

TELL YOU WHAT, IF YOU FANCY SOME REAL COMPANY, YOU COULD ALWAYS COME DOWN THE PUB WITH ME AND THE LADS.
NO THANKS. I'VE GOT SHIT TO DO.

WHAT'D YOU FUCKING *SAY?*

OI! I *ASKED YOU* SOMETHING.

I *SAID* WHAT'D YOU FUCKING'...

...SAY?!

BEER

HEY, LOOK, MAN. I--

SMACK

--FUCK!

SHIT! I... I THOUGHT THAT WAS *EMPTY*.

WAIT, MATE!
I THOUGHT IT WAS EMPTY!
LOCK
IT WAS AN ACCIDENT!
C'MON, MATE!
SHOVE
JUST DON'T TELL YOUR MUM!
LET'S TALK THIS OVER LIKE MEN!
JUST OPEN UP!
TJ?
SLAM
THUD
FUCKIN' IDIOT, TEEJ.
Petey ›
Hey TJ, could u come over and give me a hand later? I need help with this project ://
I CAN'T HAVE FUCKED THIS UP.
LIKE I FUCKIN' MESS EVERYTHING UP...
...I CAN'T HAVE FUCKED THIS UP.

Competition
OPEN
Down
Schedule & Submis
Prizes
OK PRIYA... SO WE MAY NOT BE ALLOWED OUT RIGHT NOW...

...BUT AT LEAST THAT GIVES YOU SOME FREE TIME.
LET'S MAKE THE MOST OF IT.

TUESDAY

WEDNESDAY

THURSDAY

NAILED IT.
PRIYA!*
*TRANSLATED FROM PUNJABI.

COME DOWN AND HELP ME WITH THESE DISHES!

COMING!

HEY, REHAN. WHERE YOU AT?!

ON MY WAY, JAIDEEP! JUST NEEDED A PISS.

...I JUST KNOW IT WAS ONE OF THEM.*
*TRANSLATED FROM PUNJABI.

IF JAIDEEP DOESN'T KNOW WHAT HAPPENED TO THE LAPTOP, I'M NOT SURE WHAT WE CAN DO.

YOUR MASI WAS FOOLISH TO TRUST YOU WITH THAT LAPTOP.
YOU'LL CALL YOUR MASAR IMMEDIATELY TO APOLOGISE THEN SAVE UP TO PAY HIM BACK IN DUE TIME.

ARE YOU KIDDING ME?!
I'M TELLING YOU, IT WAS LITERALLY JAIDEEP OR HIS SHADY ASS MATES!

LOOK, PRIYA...
...I'M SURE YOUR BROTHER WILL DO EVERYTHING TO HELP...
...BUT HE IS A GROWING YOUNG MAN, AND WE CAN'T HOLD HIM ACCOUNTABLE FOR THE ACTIONS OF OTHERS.
BUT YOU'D HOLD ME ACCOUNT-ABLE?!

SERIOUSLY?!
WELL THEN, YOU CAN HOLD YOURSELVES ACCOUNTABLE FOR WHEN I MOVE OUT AND...
...AND...
...NEVER SPEAK TO ANY OF YOU EVER AGAIN!
YOU KNOW WHAT?
FORGET IT. I JUST NEED SOME AIR.
PRIYA...
COME BACK NOW!
YOU'RE STILL GROUNDED FROM YOUR PARTY!
PRIYA?!
I THOUGHT IT WAS YOU!

TJ? WHAT THE HELL ARE YOU DOING HERE?
WHAT HAPPENED TO YOUR FACE?

WELL, FIRSTLY, I'M HERE COS I DIDN'T THINK THE LADIES WOULD FANCY ME MUCH DOWN TOWN WITH A MUG LIKE THIS...

...AND SECONDLY, A BEER CAN HAPPENED TO MY FACE...

PING
23:14
NEW MESSAGE
MUM
PING

Hey TJ are you out tonight? Do you want me to keep you some food?

ARE YOU OK?

YEAH, I'LL BE FINE.
I MEAN, IF YOU THINK I'M BAD, YOU SHOULD SEE WHAT THE BEER CAN LOOKS LIKE.
MY EYE **REALLY** DID A NUMBER ON ITS PULL TAB THINGY...

WHAT'RE YOU DOING HERE ALONE SO LATE ANYWAY?
DON'T YOU KNOW THERE COULD BE SOME DODGY CHARACTERS AROUND?
I DUNNO.

I HAD A FIGHT WITH MY FAMILY. A PRETTY **BIG** FIGHT.
I WAS TRYING TO STAND UP FOR MYSELF, BUT I THINK I TOOK IT A BIT TOO FAR.
THOUGH, TO BE FAIR, I WAS NEVER REALLY TAUGHT HOW TO STAND UP FOR MY-SELF.

THEY'VE JUST GOT **SUCH** OUTDATED IDEAS ABOUT THE ROLE OF A WOMAN.
AND NOT ONCE HAVE ANY OF THEM EVER CARED TO ASK WHAT I THINK OR WANT.
THEIR IDEA OF SUCCESS IS FOR ME TO JUST HAVE LOTS OF MONEY AND KIDS IN EXACTLY THE WAY THEY TELL ME TO DO IT.

TO BE HONEST, I'D BE SURPRISED IF I'M ALLOWED BACK ON THE COURSE AFTER TONIGHT.

THAT'S ROUGH. FEELS LIKE I'VE GOT THE OPPOSITE PROBLEM.

FEELS ALL ANYONE THINKS I'M CAPABLE OF IS LAYING DOWN IN A GUTTER AND WASTING AWAY.

WORST PART IS, SOMETIMES I FEEL CLOSE TO AGREEING WITH THEM.

DO YOU WANT TO QUIT [RE]START?

DEFINITELY NOT! THERE'S SO MUCH I WOULD LIKE TO DO, TJ... THOUGH MY PARENTS NEVER LET ME.

HAVE YOU EVER JUST TOLD THEM ABOUT ALL THIS? AND, LIKE, NOT VIA A SHOUTING MATCH.
I MEAN, I KINDA HAVE. I TRIED. BUT...
...NO, NOT REALLY.

MAYBE RIGHT NOW THEY JUST THINK THEY KNOW WHAT'S BEST FOR YOU, MORE THAN YOU DO.

AND YOU'VE JUST GOTTA SHOW 'EM THAT'S NOT THE CASE. NOT IN AN ANGRY WAY. BE CALM AND CLEAR. GOD KNOWS GETTIN' ANGRY HAS NEVER WORKED OUT FOR ME.

YEAH, OK. THANKS, TEEJ. I'LL GIVE IT A GO.

!
OI! PRIYA!
PRIYA!

WHAT THE HELL IS THIS?!
RUNNING OFF TO MEET CHAVS IN THE NIGHT?
THE HELL IS WRONG WITH YOU?!

IGNORE HIM, TJ.
HEY, MAN!
LOOK, I DON'T WANT ANY TROUBLE, MATE.
HE'S JUST MY IDIOT BROTHER.
AND DON'T CALL HIM A CHAV, YOU JUDGEMENTAL PRICK.

PRIYA, WE'RE GOING HOME NOW.
MUM AND DAD ARE WORRIED SICK.
THIS IS NO WAY TO BE ACTING.

EXCUSE ME.
SLAP
BUT YOU HAVE **NO RIGHT** TO HAVE ANY SAY IN WHAT I DO.

YOU THINK YOU'RE HELPING ME?!

WELL, WHERE WERE YOU WHENEVER *I* WANTED TO GO OUT AND YOU LEFT ME TO DO ALL THE HOUSEWORK?
WHERE WERE YOU WHEN I WAS DOING MY APPLICATION FOR THE TRIP OF A LIFETIME?
OH YEAH, YOU NICKED THE INTERNET!

THEN YOUR MATE STOLE MASAR'S LAPTOP AND YOU JUST SAT BACK AND LET MUM AND DAD BLAME ME.
OR HOW ABOUT WHEN I WAS SICK AND NEEDED YOUR HELP?
PRIYA, I...

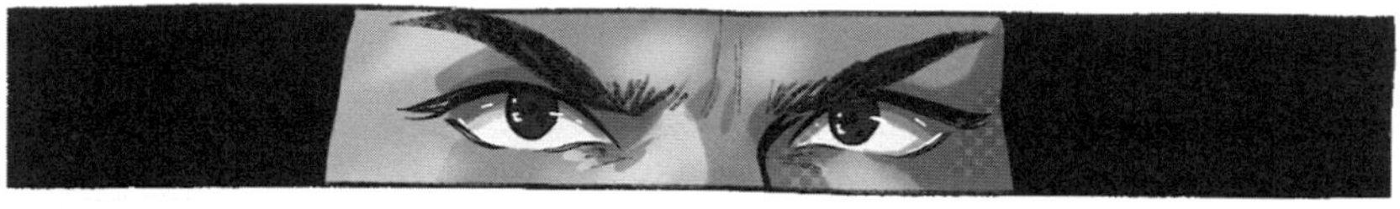

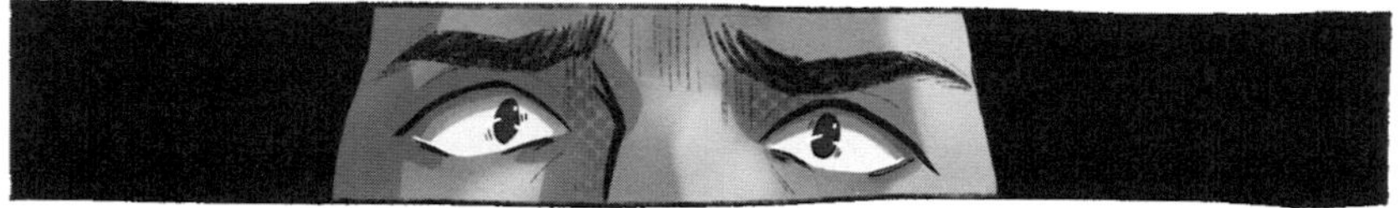

Hey Georgie, I think I need some help, something happened. you free tomorrow?

STAGE FIVE

START MOVING

"MY APPROACH IS JUST FEARLESS. I'M NOT AFRAID TO TRY ANYTHING."
STORMZY*

*STORMZY IS A BRITISH RAPPER, SINGER AND SONGWRITER.

"THE RISK OF A WRONG DECISION IS PREFERABLE TO THE TERROR OF INDECISION"*
IT'S TIME TO GET GOING.

IF YOU DON'T MOVE, NOTHING WILL HAPPEN.

MOVEMENT CREATES MOMENTUM AND MOMENTUM CREATES OPPORTUNITIES.

SEE EVERY EXPERIENCE AS AN OPPORTUNITY TO LEARN AND GUIDE YOUR FUTURE ACTIONS. THIS MINDSET WILL FREE YOU AS YOU GAIN VALUABLE LESSONS, EVEN FROM FAILURE.

OK, SO WHAT'S THE HARDEST PART OF ALL THIS?

*MAIMONIDES, AN INFLUENTIAL JEWISH SCHOLAR FROM THE MIDDLE AGES.

IT'S GOTTA BE STARTING OUT.

YEAH. I ALWAYS WANT EVERYTHING TO START PERFECTLY, WHICH CAN BE EXHAUSTING.

OR I FIND AN EXCUSE THAT I NEED TO DO SOMETHING BEFORE I CAN START.

EXACTLY.

22
IF WE START SMALL...

30
...THE BIGGER MOVES WILL OFTEN TAKE CARE OF THEM-SELVES!

SO IT'S OFTEN BETTER TO TACKLE THINGS HEAD ON AND SIMPLY GET GOING.
THIS COULD BE AS SIMPLE AS SENDING ONE EMAIL...
...OR WRITING A LIST OF THINGS YOU NEED TO DO.

SHRUG
WHERE'S TJ?

1. BREAK DOWN TASKS INTO SMALL EASY STEPS

2. DO THE WORST THINGS FIRST EVERY DAY

3. BE HONEST WITH YOURSELF: IF YOU'RE STUCK GET HELP

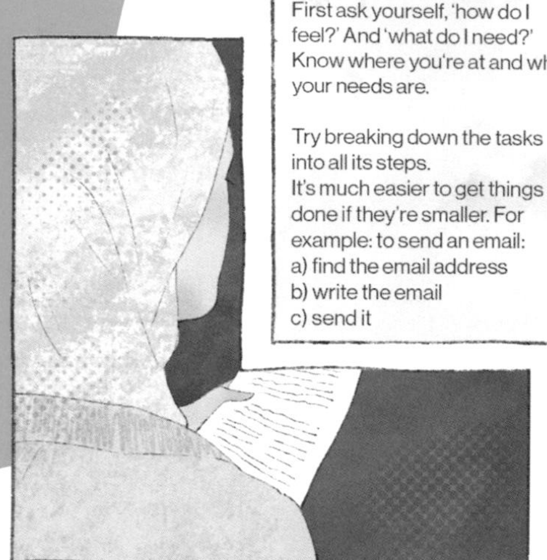

First ask yourself, 'how do I feel?' And 'what do I need?' Know where you're at and what your needs are.

Try breaking down the tasks into all its steps.
It's much easier to get things done if they're smaller. For example: to send an email:
a) find the email address
b) write the email
c) send it

"USE MEASURES LIKE THESE TO MAKE TASKS LESS INTIMIDATING. THINK 'WHAT'S THE WORST THAT COULD HAPPEN?'
"IT'S SO TEMPTING TO AVOID THINGS YOU DON'T WANT TO DO. BUT ALL YOU GET FROM GIVING IN TO THAT FEELING IS GUILT.

WOBBLE
WOBBLE
"THERE WILL BE TIMES WHERE YOU'LL BE AFRAID TO MESS UP GREAT OPPORTUNITIES.

"...THEY'RE USUALLY NOT AS IMPORTANT OR SERIOUS AS WE THINK...

"...AND THERE'LL BE PLENTY MORE OPPORTUNITIES TO COME!

HAHAHA HaHa
"REMEMBER, WE'RE LEARNING, SO THERE IS ONLY OPPORTUNITY!"

"ANOTHER GOOD TACTIC...
06:07
"...IS TO DO THE THING YOU DON'T WANT TO **FIRST THING** IN THE MORNING.
"THIS GIVES YOU MORE ENERGY TO FACE IT...

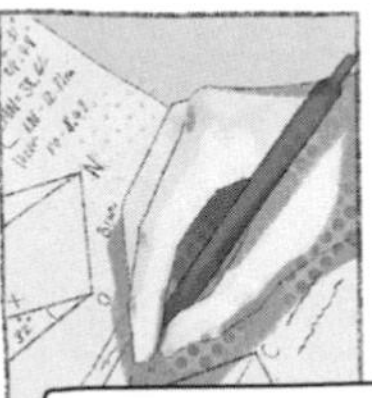
"...AND THEN YOU CAN ENJOY THE REST OF THE DAY GUILT-FREE.

ZZZ
ZZZZ

"MANY PEOPLE HAVE MORE WILLPOWER EARLIER AND IT WEARS DOWN OVER THE DAY. THERE ARE ALSO LESS DISTRACTIONS EARLY IN THE MORNING.
Creak
CREAK

21:10
"THOUGH SOME FIND THEY HAVE MORE ENERGY AND FOCUS LATE AT NIGHT WHEN IT'S QUIET. BUT YOU HAVE TO MAKE SURE YOU MAKE SPACE FOR THAT TOO.

"BE HONEST WITH YOURSELF. IF YOU'RE STUCK, ASK YOURSELF 'WHY DON'T I WANT TO DO THIS?' FOR EXAMPLE, YOU MAY GET NERVOUS ABOUT WRITING EMAILS CORRECTLY, SO ASK SOMEONE FOR HELP.

"USE PEOPLE, PLACES OR PRODUCTS TO HELP YOU. IF YOU REALLY STRUGGLE BY YOURSELF, FIND A PLACE WHICH MAKES IT EASIER FOR YOU.
"PERHAPS A CAFE OR LIBRARY. REACH OUT TO PEOPLE WHO CAN HELP.

"SOME PEOPLE MAKE THINGS HARDER. AVOID THEM. SEEK OUT THOSE WHO HELP.

"PRODUCTS ARE THINGS LIKE DIARIES, POST-IT NOTES, APPS AND NOTICEBOARDS."

TAKE OPPORTUNITIES

THEY MIGHT ONLY COME ONCE

WHEN WE DO OUR BEST AND ARE POLITE, OPPORTUNITIES WILL COME OUR WAY.

I LOVE THIS QUOTE FROM SENECA THE YOUNGER.
"LUCK IS WHAT HAPPENS WHEN PREPARATION MEETS OPPOR-TUNITY."
WHO'S SENECA? SOUNDS LIKE A DJ.

HE WAS A ROMAN PHILOSOPHER FROM EMPEROR NERO'S REIGN.
HE WAS ONE OF THE LEADING INTELLECTUAL FIGURES OF THE TIME.

WAS HE SMARTER THAN SENECA THE ELDER?

MY POINT IS...
...WE'VE GOT TO STRETCH OURSELVES OUTSIDE OF OUR COMFORT ZONES...
...AND INTO THOSE OPPORTUNITIES.

THAT'S A GREAT THOUGHT, PRIYA.
NUDGE

REMEMBER, GUYS, IF YOU'RE STRUGGLING WITH ANY OF THIS, ASK FOR HELP.
SOMEONE UNEXPECTED MAY PROVIDE A COMPLETELY FRESH VIEW. REMEMBER THE POWER OF DIFFERENCE!

OK! LET'S RECAP OPPORTUNITIES. IF SOMEONE'S GIVING YOU ADVICE, LISTEN!

YOU NEVER KNOW WHAT YOU MAY FIND OUT OR WHERE IT COULD LEAD TO.

EVEN IF IT'S HARD TO LISTEN TO, THEY'RE GIVING YOU A GIFT. YOU'LL LEARN SOMETHING.

BE CURIOUS ABOUT THE PEOPLE AROUND YOU.

"ASK THEM QUESTIONS. AND IF YOU DON'T UNDERSTAND, SAY IT. DON'T FAKE IT!

"WHEN YOU SHOW AN INTEREST, YOU'LL BE SURPRISED WHAT CAN HAPPEN. PEOPLE WILL MAKE CONNECTIONS FOR YOU.

"IF YOU'RE OFFERED ADVICE, A CHAT OR A JOB, FOLLOW UP! ALWAYS SEND A RESPONSE OR A THANK YOU.

Art opportunities

To: S.Hewitts@graphics.a

Dear Mrs Hewitts,

I've decided to follow your

"YOU NEVER KNOW WHEN IT MIGHT BE USEFUL IN THE FUTURE.

"IF YOU'RE OFFERED MORE WORK OR RESPONSIBILITY, DO IT! YOU'LL LEARN AND GROW FASTER.

"BUT ALWAYS BE MINDFUL OF YOUR DREAM AND YOUR VALUES. SOME OPPORTUNITIES JUST DON'T FIT WITH WHO YOU ARE AND WHERE YOU WANT TO GO."

MAKE OPPORTUNITIES

BE PROACTIVE, ENGAGE WITH PEOPLE, SHOW INTEREST

MATCH YOUR ACTIVITIES TO YOUR DAILY ENERGY FLOW

OKAY GUYS, I'D LIKE YOU TO MEET ZADIE, THE CEO OF A STARTUP. SHE'S BUILT A TEAM OF A HUNDRED IN THREE YEARS.

"WE MET WHEN WE WERE OUT RUNNING ONE DAY!"

HI GUYS. NICE TO MEET YOU ALL.
I'VE HEARD GREAT THINGS ABOUT EVERY-ONE.

I GATHER YOU'RE LOOKING FOR TIPS TO GET GOING.
IT'S IMPORTANT TO KNOW HOW TO GET THE MOST OUT OF YOURSELF. AS A LEADER, IF I DON'T GET GOING, NO ONE ELSE WILL!

06:30
"SINCE I'M AN EARLY RISER, I DO MY BEST THINKING IN THE MORNING.

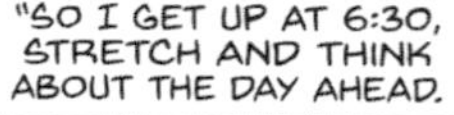

"SO I GET UP AT 6:30, STRETCH AND THINK ABOUT THE DAY AHEAD.

BZZZZ

07:30
"I THEN FIRE OUT EMAILS COVERING WHAT I NEED MY TEAM TO DO."

09:00

09:30
"I'M IN THE OFFICE AT 9.30 AND I'M IN MEETINGS UNTIL LUNCH, SO I NEED FOCUS AND ENERGY TO LISTEN AND THINK.

13:00
"I'M PRETTY USELESS AFTER LUNCH, SO I MAKE SURE I SCHEDULE TIME TO CHECK MY EMAILS. IT DOESN'T REQUIRE ME TO THINK TOO MUCH BUT NEEDS TO BE DONE.
"I OFTEN MEDITATE FOR HALF AN HOUR TO RECHARGE.

"BETWEEN 3 AND 6PM I'M FULL OF ENERGY AND READY TO TALK TO THE TEAM OR CLIENTS. I KNOW I'M IN A GOOD SPACE TO GIVE ENERGY TO OTHERS AND MOTIVATE PEOPLE.

"ARE YOU A MORNING PERSON OR A NIGHT OWL?

cLINK

"KNOWING YOUR ENERGY FLOW CAN HELP YOU DO THE RIGHT TASKS AT THE RIGHT TIME FOR YOU.
"KNOWING WHEN I WORK BEST HELPS ME REACH AN IDEAL WORK-LIFE BALANCE. I KNOW MY EVENINGS WILL BE FREE TO UNWIND."

WHY NOT EXPLORE?

BE BRAVE, REACH OUT AND START MOVING...

ALL RIGHT, GUYS. TIME TO MAKE THIS REAL FOR YOU.
FIRST, I WANT YOU TO WRITE DOWN A LIST OF ALL THE THINGS YOU MUST DO AND WHEN YOU'RE DONE, UNDERLINE THE THREE MOST IMPORTANT.

WHERE'S THAT PEN?
"NEXT, HOW ARE YOU GOING TO START MOVING ON THESE THREE THINGS? BREAK THEM INTO INDIVIDUAL STEPS, LIKE HOW YOU WILL START, WHEN AND WHERE?

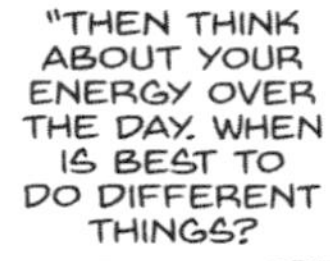

"THEN THINK ABOUT YOUR ENERGY OVER THE DAY. WHEN IS BEST TO DO DIFFERENT THINGS?

"WHAT CAN YOU DO TO HELP YOU BE AT YOUR BEST?

"AND FINALLY...

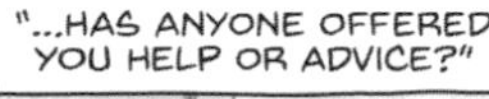

"...HAS ANYONE OFFERED YOU HELP OR ADVICE?"

I MET WITH SOMEONE AGES AGO. COULD I STILL FOLLOW UP WITH THEM?

YES! ABSOLUTELY. BE BRAVE AND REACH OUT. IF YOU DON'T HEAR BACK, FOLLOW UP AGAIN.

THIS SPACE IS FOR YOUR REFLECTIONS | DATE: ....

MAKE A TO-DO LIST AND UNDERLINE THREE KEY ACTIONS

Write down a list of the first things you need to get done (small steps, remember). Highlight three actions you feel comfortable with tackling first. What's the most important?

THIS SPACE IS FOR YOUR REFLECTIONS / DATE: ....

CAN YOU BREAK DOWN THESE THREE ACTIONS EVEN MORE?

This could be requesting a school/college prospectus or enquiring about interships/apprenticeships. Think about how, when and where you feel you can, or want to, focus on this.

THIS SPACE IS FOR YOUR REFLECTIONS | DATE: ....

WHEN ARE YOUR ENERGY LEVELS HIGH AND LOW IN THE DAY?

Think about times in the day when you have clarity and courage to do what you need to. For example, I think clearly early in the morning or I'm creative late at night.

THIS SPACE IS FOR YOUR REFLECTIONS / DATE: ....

REMIND YOURSELF OF ANY ADVICE YOU'VE RECEIVED

Think of all the people you've met who have offered advice or guidance. Keep in touch and follow up with them when you're ready. You never know where it might lead!

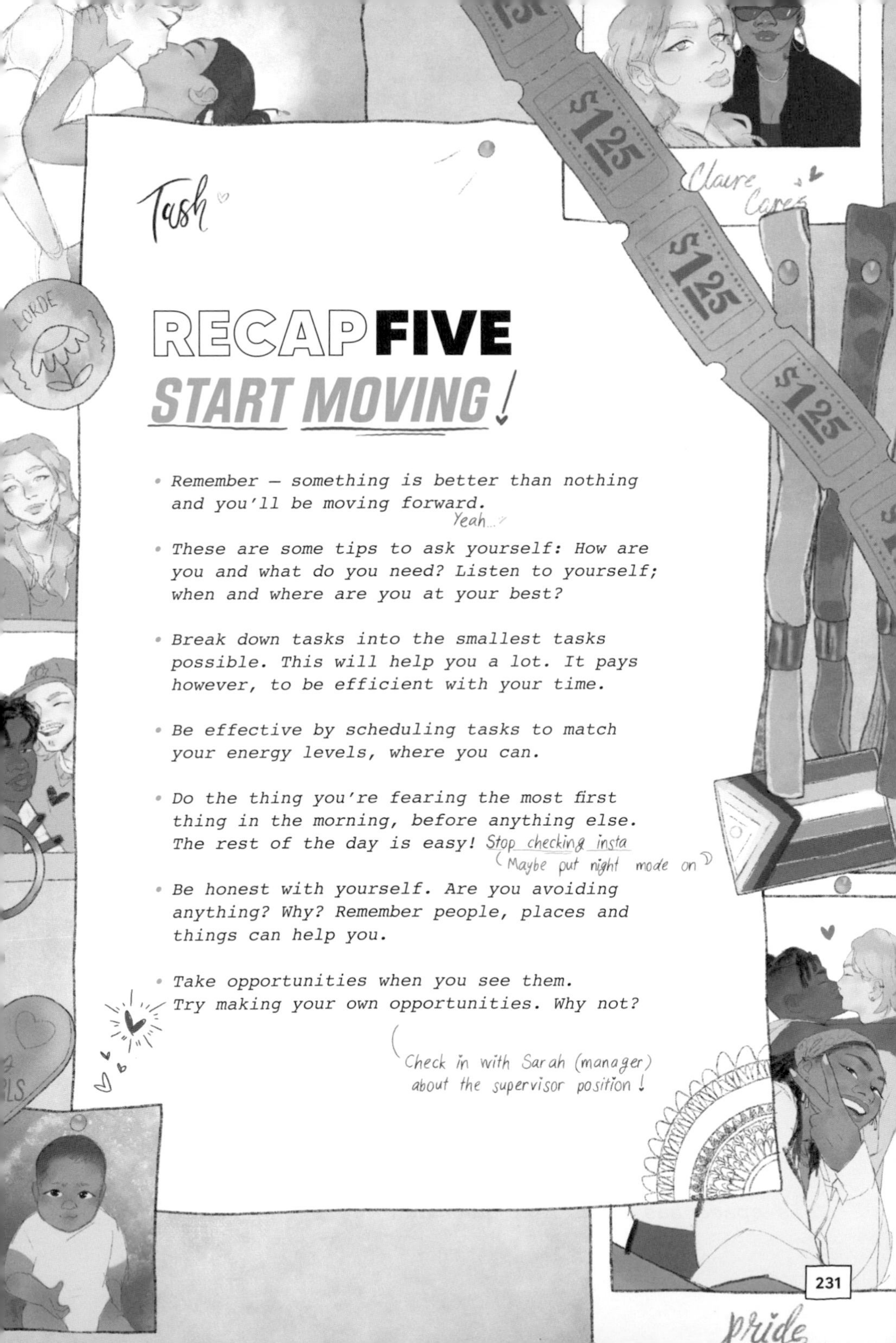

RECAP FIVE
START MOVING!

- Remember – something is better than nothing and you'll be moving forward. *Yeah...*
- These are some tips to ask yourself: How are you and what do you need? Listen to yourself; when and where are you at your best?
- Break down tasks into the smallest tasks possible. This will help you a lot. It pays however, to be efficient with your time.
- Be effective by scheduling tasks to match your energy levels, where you can.
- Do the thing you're fearing the most first thing in the morning, before anything else. The rest of the day is easy! *Stop checking insta (Maybe put night mode on)*
- Be honest with yourself. Are you avoiding anything? Why? Remember people, places and things can help you.
- Take opportunities when you see them. Try making your own opportunities. Why not?

(Check in with Sarah (manager) about the supervisor position!

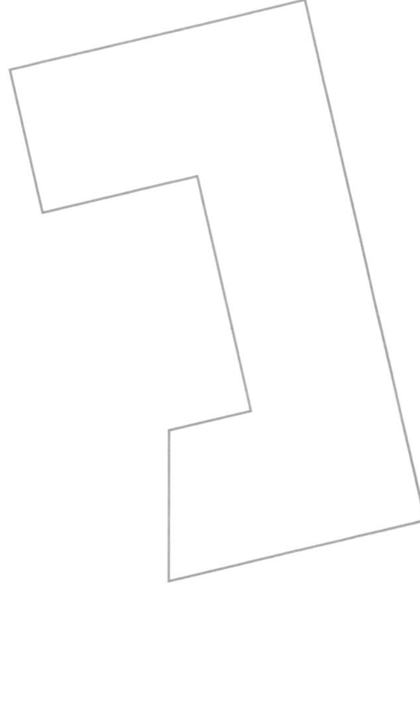

This space has been left for you.

+99 NEW NOTIFICATIONS

1) NEW MESSAGE
OM CLARE

TASH! DID YOU WANT TO GRAB A COFFEE?

SORRY, GIRLS. I'M NOT UP FOR A CHAT.

HEY, NEERA!
HI, TJ. HOW ARE YOU?
I'M SORRY I DIDN'T MAKE IT. I'VE GOT...
...I'VE GOT A LOT ON AT THE MOMENT.
TJ, ARE YOU ALL RIGHT?
YEAH, YEAH. I JUST WALKED INTO A LAMPPOST.
TJ, I UNDERSTAND YOU MAY BE IN SOME TROUBLE. I WANT YOU TO KNOW THERE ARE PEOPLE WHO CAN HELP YOU.
UH, THAT'S ALL RIGHT, THANKS. I DON'T NEED NO HELP LIKE THAT.
LISTEN, YOU'RE A GREAT GUY, TJ. YOU'RE FUNNY, YOU MAKE EVERYONE AROUND YOU FEEL BRIGHTER, AND YOU'RE SMARTER THAN YOU GIVE YOURSELF CREDIT FOR.
I'M NOT ALL THAT...
YOU ARE.
I KNOW HOW WELL YOU GET ON WITH THE OTHERS, SO IT MIGHT BE A GOOD IDEA TO REACH OUT TO THEM.
HELP CAN COME FROM ALL KINDS OF PLACES.
YOU SHOULDN'T BE AFRAID TO RELY ON OTHERS. WE WORRY ABOUT YOU WHEN YOU DISAPPEAR.
WE JUST WANT YOU TO LET US KNOW YOU'RE OKAY.
(6) MISSED CALLS FROM MUM

LATER THAT DAY...

RIIIP

HEY, MUM.

TJ! OH MY GOSH!

WHAT HAPPENED?! ARE YOU OKAY?
I'M FINE, MUM.
DID YOU GET IN A FIGHT OR SOMETHING?

NO. NO, MUM, IT WASN'T A FIGHT...
...IT WAS BARRY.

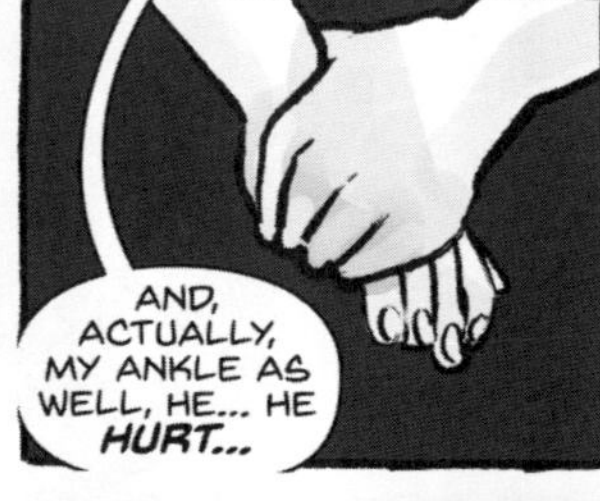
AND, ACTUALLY, MY ANKLE AS WELL, HE... HE HURT...

...LOOK, WE NEED TO TALK ABOUT SOME STUFF...

Gooble Internship
Deadline Extension
THANKS FOR ALL YOUR HELP, AUNTIE DEBBIE.
PETER...
YES?
I KNOW THINGS HAVE BEEN HARD SINCE YOUR FATHER PASSED.

I JUST THINK YOU SHOULD KNOW THAT HE WOULD BE SO PROUD OF YOU.
FOR WHAT?
FOR STEPPING UP.
THANKS, AUNTIE. I'LL SEE YOU TOMORROW.

KNOCK KNOCK

"I'LL GET IT."

HEY, MAN.
23

TJ... YOU ALL RIGHT?
I, UH, FELL ON A BEER CAN.

RIGHT... MUST HAVE BEEN SOME FALL.
23

LISTEN, MAN I'M REALLY SORRY ABOUT HOW I'VE BEEN ACTING.
IT AIN'T RIGHT AND I JUST WANT TO SAY SORRY, FOR REAL.

I WANT TO MAKE IT UP TO YOU...

...IF THAT'S ALL RIGHT? I CAN STILL HELP OUT WITH THAT PROJECT YOU WERE DOING.

IT'S TOO LATE, TEEJ.
!
HEY, C'MON, DON'T SAY THAT! I WOULD'VE COME OVER SOONER!

NAH, NOT LIKE THAT!
I MEAN IT'S TOO LATE FOR THE PROJECT.

I ASKED FOR AN EXTENSION BUT I'M STILL WAITING FOR A REPLY. I DON'T EVEN KNOW IF I HAVE THE TIME NOW--

!
PING

17:00
(1) New E
Dear Mr...

WELL?

LOOKS LIKE YOU'RE GONNA HAVE TO KEEP YOUR PROMISE AFTER ALL.
I GOT THE EXTENSION!

WHOOSH
YES! THAT'S WHAT'S UP, PETEY BOY!

AHEM! THING ONE, THING TWO, THIS IS TJ.

TJ, THESE ARE THE GREMLINS.

MY MUM'S RESTING IN HER ROOM SO I'VE GOT TO WATCH THEM.
WELL EASY! I'LL WATCH 'EM AND YOU GET ON WITH YOUR WORK!
I'M TELLING MUM YOU CALLED US NAMES.

WHY DOES YOUR BOYFRIEND HAVE A BLACK EYE?

SMACK

WestMALL

HEY, TASH!
HEY, YAS!
HOWDY, ANNIE.
GOOD TO SEE YOU, ***TRISH.***

SO, WHAT'S NEW WITH YOU?
NOTHING, REALLY.

HAVE YOU SPOKEN TO ANY OF YOUR FRIENDS LIKE WE TALKED ABOUT?
NOT YET...

...I DON'T REALLY FEEL UP TO IT.
WHAT'S THIS ABOUT?

I, URM, HAD A PROBLEM WITH A POST ON MY INSTA.
HAVE YOU THOUGHT ABOUT DELETING IT?

OH NO, LIKE IT'S MY POST--
NO, I MEAN DELETING THE WHOLE APP.

WHY WOULD I DO THAT?
I MEAN...
...IF IT'S NOT BRINGING YOU ANY ACTUAL JOY...
...AND TO BE HONEST, IT SEEMS TO BE MAKING YOU MISERABLE...
...WHY KEEP SOMETHING LIKE THAT IN YOUR LIFE?
I NEVER THOUGHT OF IT LIKE THAT.
I GUESS I JUST THINK I'D BE MISSING OUT ON SO MUCH.
LIKE WHAT?
LIKE... ERM...
OH NO...

GONE
WHAT'S GOING ON, ANDI? WHY THE SUDDEN URGE TO BUY A PIN BADGE?
I SAW SOME GIRLS I DON'T WANT TO TALK TO.
WHY? ARE THEY BEING MEAN TO YOU?
NO...
...I MEAN... I DON'T THINK THEY ARE, BUT...
BUT?
BUT THEY MAKE ME FEEL SO ANXIOUS, AND I ***COMPLETELY*** EMBARRASSED MYSELF IN FRONT OF THEM.
REMEMBER WHEN WE FIRST MET AND I GOT YOUR NAME WRONG?
YEAH, IT'S KIND OF OUR THING NOW.
WELL, THIS IS JUST LIKE THAT.
I EMBARRASSED MYSELF IN FRONT OF YOU BUT THEN WE TALKED IT OUT AND NOW LOOK! YOU SHOULD TRY SPEAKING TO THEM.
GET IT OFF YOUR CHEST!
SPEAKING AS AN ENTIRELY OBJECTIVE THIRD PARTY, I THINK IT'S A GOOD IDEA.
WE'LL COME WITH YOU IF YOU WANT?

HEY, ANDI! NICE TO SEE YOU.
HEY, I JUST WANTED TO SAY SORRY I WAS SICK ON YOU THE OTHER DAY... AND THAT I CALLED YOU A GOAT. I DIDN'T MEAN IT.

OH, THAT'S OKAY! I KNEW IT WAS AN ACCIDENT.

OKAY, GOOD... BUT THERE'S ALSO SOMETHING ELSE I WANTED TO TALK ABOUT.

I DIDN'T LIKE IT WHEN YOU CORRECTED MY ENGLISH.
I GET IT'S NOT MY FIRST LANGUAGE BUT THERE'S NO NEED TO BE RUDE.

OH, I'M REALLY SORRY. THAT WASN'T MY INTENTION AT ALL!

REALLY?
NOT AT ALL!

I HAVE A FRIEND WHO'S POLISH AND SHE ALWAYS WANTS ME TO CORRECT HER ENGLISH. IT'S LIKE A RUNNING JOKE NOW.

BUT I GUESS BECAUSE IT DIDN'T BOTHER HER, I JUST DIDN'T THINK HOW IT MIGHT BE HURTFUL TO OTHERS.
I'M SO, SO SORRY IT CAME OUT THAT WAY. I WAS JUST TRYING TO BE FRIENDLY!

SO... YOU WEREN'T MAKING FUN OF ME?

WHAT?! NO!
OF COURSE NOT!
WE THINK YOU'RE SO COOL. I MEAN, I WOULDN'T HAVE THE GUTS TO STUDY ABROAD!

WELL, I, UH... I'M SORRY FOR JUMPING TO CONCLUSIONS.
PROUD
IT'S OK. I'M SORRY WE MADE YOU UNCOMFORTABLE!
FRIENDS? WE CAN HAVE LUNCH TOGETHER ON MONDAY IF YOU'D LIKE?

SURE, I'D LIKE THAT.

SORRY FOR JUMPING OUT AT YOU IN A SHOP, TOO...

JUMP OUT AT US WHENEVER YOU WANT!

ANDI! I AM SO PROUD OF YOU! THAT WAS AMAZING!

AWH, THANKS, GUYS. I FEEL SO MUCH BETTER NOW.

I DON'T KNOW IF I COULD'VE DONE THAT!

TAP TAP
TAP

Sophie
Can I call you?
PING
Still in disbelief that today actually happened, who am I lol <3 u guys
Never would
@Andi you're awesome!!

SOPHIE?
HEY, HUN.
WHAT'S UP?

I WANT TO APOLOGISE FOR WHAT I SAID TO YOU AND HOW I'VE ACTED.
SOPHIE...
I SHOULD HAVE REALISED YOU WERE LOOKING OUT FOR ME AS WELL.
I WAS JUST SO ANGRY AND ENDED UP LASHING OUT.
IT'S OKAY.
DO YOU WANT TO TELL ME WHAT HAPPENED?

I GUESS IT HURT WHEN PRIYA DIDN'T SHOW. I UNDERSTAND WHAT HAPPENED, BUT IT HURT TO BE LEFT IN A SITUATION WHERE I NEEDED SUPPORT.
THEN WHEN YOU TOLD ME PRIYA'S SIDE, IT WAS LIKE WHAT I FELT DIDN'T MATTER.
SOPHIE, I'M SORRY. I DIDN'T REALISE YOU WERE IN SUCH A BAD PLACE. I JUST WANTED TO LOOK OUT FOR PRIYA...
...BUT I CAN SEE NOW I WENT ABOUT IT THE WRONG WAY. I THINK AT THE TIME I JUST FELT SO ALONE, I WANTED TO BE THERE FOR SOMEONE ELSE...

...I'M GLAD YOU BOTH SORTED IT OUT THOUGH.

TASH, I HAD NO IDEA YOU WOULD EVER FEEL THAT WAY!
WELL... YEAH. IT'S A WHOLE THING.

BUT I RECENTLY REALISED THAT I NEED TO BE KINDER TO MYSELF.
MAYBE YOU SHOULD TRY TO DO THE SAME?
I'LL TRY, TASH. THANK YOU FOR CHATTING WITH ME.
THAT'S OK, THANKS FOR CALLING! I'LL SEE YOU SOON, SOPH.

Callum
Clare
Kira
Mom
Momma
Nate
p-guy ;)

HEY, CLARE. CAN WE TALK? I'VE GOT SOMETHING I WANT TO TELL YOU.

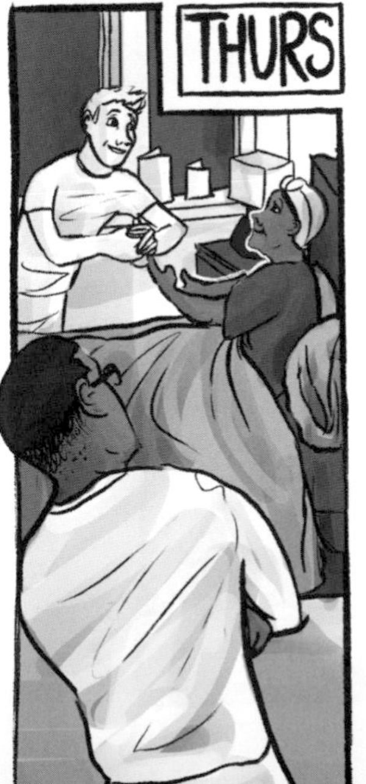

Mum

I'm here early lol. You sure I'm not making a fuss TJ? Xx

You can do this, mum. Dr Sheppard is there to understand, not judge. I'll be there to pick you up after your therapy session X

WHICH DO YOU THINK?
NEITHER. KEEP IT JUST THE JACKET. WITH YOUR NEW DO, YOU LOOK LIKE A PAPER CUT.
?
A PAPER CUT, HUH?
BUMP
WELL SHARP!
THANKS FOR ALL YOUR HELP, MAN.
I HONESTLY COULDN'T HAVE DONE IT WITHOUT YOU.
I TOLD YOU I'D MAKE A GREAT SUPERHERO.
THAT BETTER NOT BE YOUR WAY OF TELLING ME YOU GOT A CATSUIT.
YOU SURE YOU'LL BE ALL RIGHT LOOKING AFTER MY MUM AND DEALING WITH THE GREMLINS?
COURSE, MAN. SHE LOVES HER SOME TJ. AND IT CAN'T BE WORSE THAN THE TIME I DOG-SAT FOR MY COUSIN GEORGIE.
ZZZZ
LEAP OUT
I NEARLY HAD TO GET HER A NEW DOG.
WELL IF THEY ESCAPE THIS TIME...
...JUST MAKE SURE YOU GET THE SAME BREED.
GOOD LUCK, PETEY BOI.

MASHOOMA, HOW WAS WORK?*
HOW DID THEY TAKE THE NEWS OF YOUR NEW JOB, MY LITTLE ACCOUNTANT?
*TRANSLATED FROM PASHTO.

WHAT'S THE MATTER?
THERE'S SOMETHING I NEED TO TELL YOU.

WHAT IS IT? DID THEY TAKE THE JOB BACK?

NO... NO, THEY, UHM, THEY... UH...
WAS THERE A PROBLEM WITH THE APPLICATION?
DID THEY GO WITH SOMEONE ELSE?

I QUIT THE SUPERMARKET AND I DIDN'T TAKE THE ACCOUNTANCY JOB!

WHY DIDN'T YOU TAKE IT?

I DON'T KNOW... I JUST... THEY...

...THEY STILL OFFERED ME WORK IN THE SUMMER.
WHICH MEANS I DON'T HAVE TO GO BACK TO THE SUPERMARKET AND THAT STUPID MANAGER.
BUT NOW I HAVE NO INCOME, AND UNI APPLICATIONS ARE COMING UP WHICH MEANS INTERVIEWS AND TRAVEL EXPENSES AND WE CAN'T AFFORD--

SHHH, IT'S ALL RIGHT.
WHY DON'T YOU WANT TO DO THE INTERNSHIP?

IT'S JUST NOT WHAT I WANT FOR ME. I JUST...

...I JUST WANT TO DRAW.

HA HA HA HA HA HA HA HA

WHY ARE YOU LAUGHING? IT'S NOT FUNNY!
NO, MASHOOMA. WE'RE NOT LAUGHING AT YOU.
WELL, IT IS A LITTLE BIT FUNNY.

AREN'T YOU DISAPPOINTED IN ME FOR GIVING UP A PROPER JOB?
WHY WOULD YOU SAY THAT?

BECAUSE IT'S WHY WE CAME HERE, ISN'T IT? TO THIS COUNTRY?
SO WE COULD HAVE BETTER OPPORTUNITIES.

WE CAME HERE FOR YOUR SAFETY, YASMIN. WE WANT YOU TO FOLLOW YOUR DREAMS, AND YOU ARE!
IGNORING THEM JUST TO PLEASE US, WELL...
...THAT WOULDN'T HELP ANYONE.
...YOU'LL ONLY PLEASE US BY DOING WHAT ***YOU*** WANT.

WE WANT WHAT'S BEST FOR YOU AND YOUR BROTHER. AND IF IT'S AT THE END OF A PENCIL, SO BE IT.

ZA TA SARA MINA KOM YASMIN.
I LOVE YOU TOO.
WHATEVER YOU DECIDE...

...WORKING THERE IN THE SUMMER OR NOT, WE WILL SUPPORT YOU...

...AS LONG AS IT'S WHAT YOU WANT.

BUT I HAVE ONE CONDITION.
BABA?

I'D LIKE TO SEE SOME OF YOUR DRAWINGS. IF NOT, I KNOW YOU HIDE THEM UNDER YOUR BED, SO I'LL JUST TAKE A LOOK WHEN YOU'RE OUT.
BABA JAN!

SCHOOL

BREATHE IN

JOKE

HA
HA
HA
HA
HA
HA
HA
HA

BRIIING

HEY!
ANDI! WAIT A
SECOND.
OH, HEY,
LUCIE.

WE MISSED
YOU AT THE LAST
MEETING.
YEAH, I'M
SORRY.
TO BE HONEST,
I WAS SO ANXIOUS
TO COME, I KIND OF
SPIRALLED.

I WAS
NERVOUS
TO COME
AND TALK
TO YOU IN
THE FIRST
PLACE...
...SO I
COMPLETELY
GET IT.
REALLY? YOU
DON'T SEEM THAT
WAY AT ALL.

WELL,
THANKS, BUT
YEAH.
I'VE BEEN
TRYING REALLY
HARD TO OVERCOME
IT, BUT IT'S STILL A
BATTLE.

I KNOW
WHAT YOU
MEAN.
I REALLY
AM SORRY
FOR NOT
SHOWING.

IT'S
OK. BUT
I'D LOVE IT IF
YOU COULD
COME THIS
WEEK.
WE'VE STILL
GOT SOME
PLACES LEFT
ON OUR TRIP TO
ICELAND IF
YOU'RE FEELING
UP TO IT!
OKAY,
YEAH. I'LL BE
THERE!

AWESOME!
OH, AND
ANDI?
YEAH?
DON'T
STRESS TOO
MUCH ABOUT THE
CLUB. WE'RE NOT AS
SCARY AS WE
SEEM.

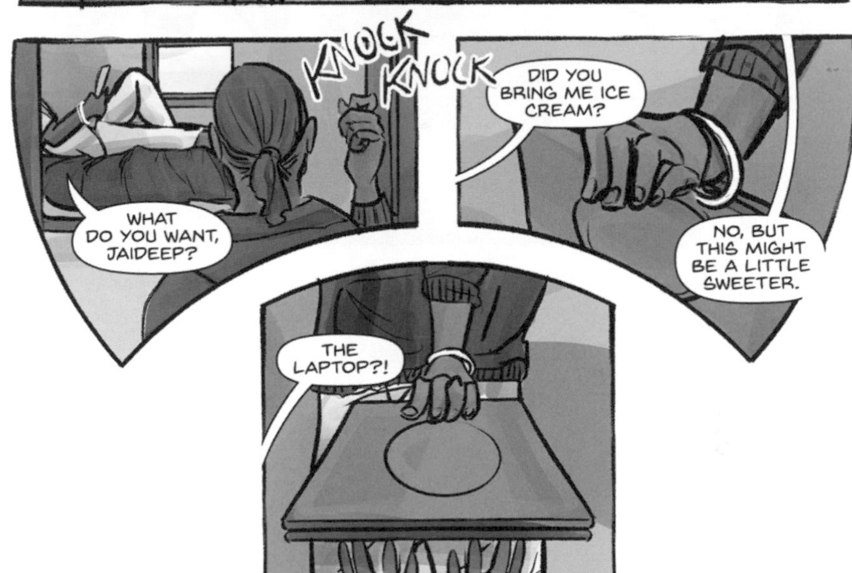
KNOCK KNOCK
WHAT DO YOU WANT, JAIDEEP?
DID YOU BRING ME ICE CREAM?
NO, BUT THIS MIGHT BE A LITTLE SWEETER.
THE LAPTOP?!

YEAH, BUT I COULDN'T SAVE IT...

THANKS FOR TRYING ANYWAY.
SAFE TO SAY REHAN WON'T BE HANGING OUT HERE AGAIN.

ON THE BRIGHT SIDE THE HARD DRIVE SEEMS TO BE INTACT...
...WHICH MEANS MASAR HAS NOTHING TO COMPLAIN ABOUT AFTER DAD GIVES HIM A FANCY NEW LAPTOP AND ALL HIS OLD FILES.
IT ALSO MEANS...

OH MY GOD! MY COMPETITION ENTRY! JAIDEEP!
...IS ALSO STILL INTACT.

BUT WHAT IF THE HARD DRIVE IS ACTUALLY DAMAGED?
THE LAPTOP IS WRECKED, HOW DO YOU EVEN KNOW IT'S NOT...

OH SORRY, DID I SAY IT SEEMS TO BE INTACT? WHAT I MEANT WAS ME AND DAD JUST CAME BACK FROM THE COMPUTER SHOP...
...AND THEY SAID IT'S FINE. THEY PUT ALL THE FILES ON THIS MEMORY STICK.
JAIDEEP! GIVE IT HERE!

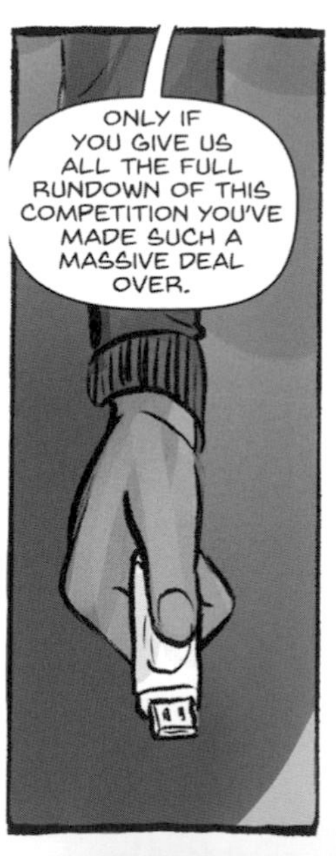
ONLY IF YOU GIVE US ALL THE FULL RUNDOWN OF THIS COMPETITION YOU'VE MADE SUCH A MASSIVE DEAL OVER.

I WANT TO PICTURE YOUR THRILLING FUTURE AS A HISTORIAN.
OH MY GOD, FINE. JUST GIVE ME THE STICK!
YOU KNOW, YOU REALLY OUGHT TO BACKUP YOUR WORK NEXT TIME.
I SWEAR, I'M THIS CLOSE TO NICKING YOUR XBOX.

HUH?

I **SAID,** YOU'VE BEEN INVITED TO ANOTHER GATHERING AT THE BARRINGTON-SMYTH'S NEXT SATURDAY.

WHAT? THERE'S NO WAY I'M GOING.

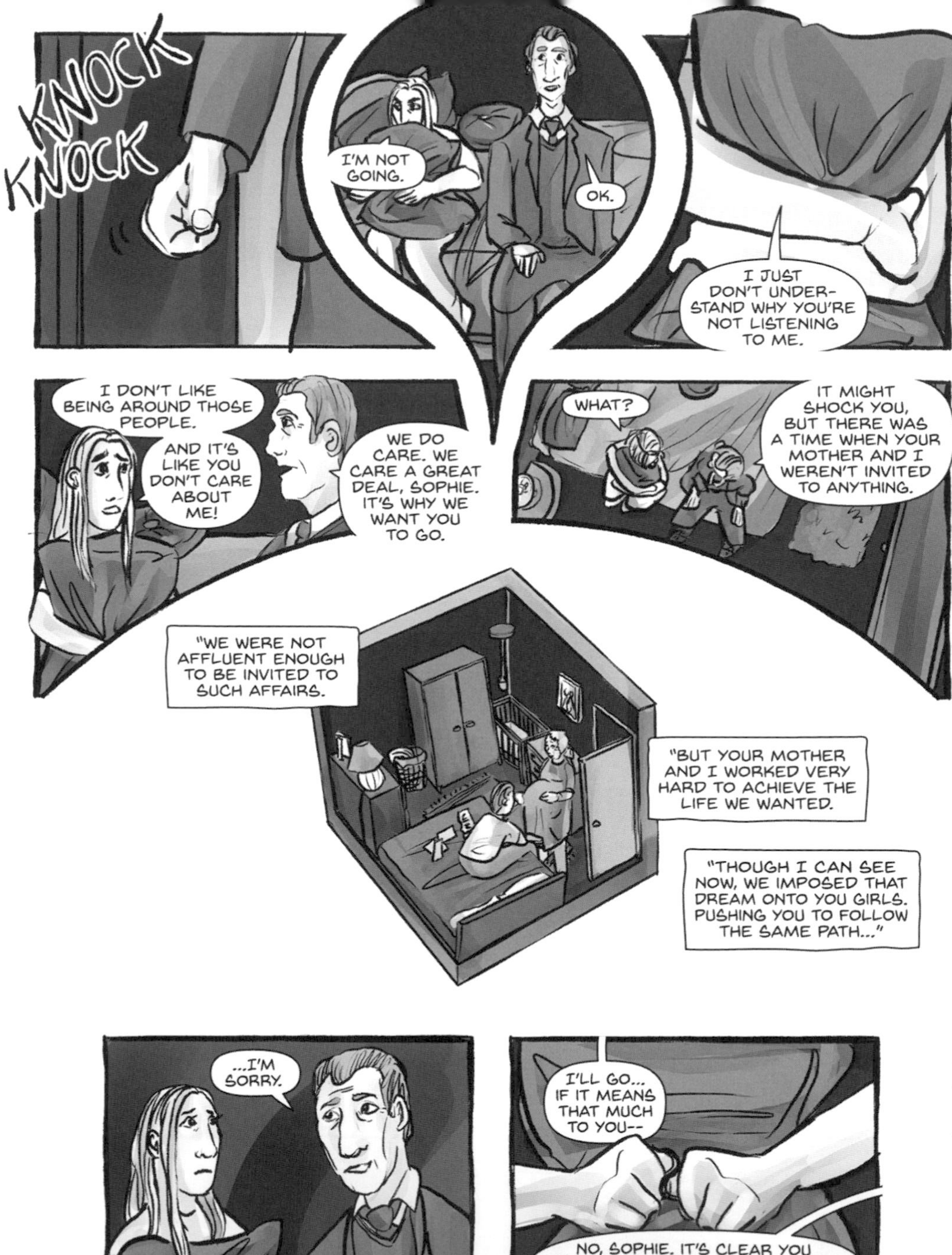

KNOCK KNOCK

I'M NOT GOING.

OK.

I JUST DON'T UNDER-STAND WHY YOU'RE NOT LISTENING TO ME.

I DON'T LIKE BEING AROUND THOSE PEOPLE.

AND IT'S LIKE YOU DON'T CARE ABOUT ME!

WE DO CARE. WE CARE A GREAT DEAL, SOPHIE. IT'S WHY WE WANT YOU TO GO.

WHAT?

IT MIGHT SHOCK YOU, BUT THERE WAS A TIME WHEN YOUR MOTHER AND I WEREN'T INVITED TO ANYTHING.

"WE WERE NOT AFFLUENT ENOUGH TO BE INVITED TO SUCH AFFAIRS.

"BUT YOUR MOTHER AND I WORKED VERY HARD TO ACHIEVE THE LIFE WE WANTED.

"THOUGH I CAN SEE NOW, WE IMPOSED THAT DREAM ONTO YOU GIRLS. PUSHING YOU TO FOLLOW THE SAME PATH..."

I'LL TELL THE BARRINGTONS YOU'RE OTHERWISE ENGAGED.

YOU GO START CARVING OUT YOUR OWN PATH.

HEY, ARE YOU FREE TONIGHT?
CALLING
PRIYA
LATER...

THANKS FOR LETTING ME COME, PRIYA.
I'M GLAD YOU CALLED! I HOPE YOU DON'T MIND MEETING SOME OF MY MATES.
HEY, GUYS! THIS IS SOPHIE.
NO, OF COURSE NOT.
LUSH NIGHT, GUYS. AND SOPHIE, IT WAS GREAT TO MEET YOU!
WE STILL ON FOR THE CINEMA NEXT SATURDAY?
YOU'RE JOINING US, RIGHT, SOPHIE?
THE CINEMA? I'D LOVE TO, IF THAT'S ALL RIGHT?
COURSE IT IS. WHO ELSE IS GONNA PAY FOR THE POPCORN?

THANKS FOR LETTING ME GET IT ALL OUT, CLARE.

YOU CAN STILL TALK TO US, REMEMBER.

19:37

I KNOW. I'VE GOT MY HOT NEW PIECE OF TECH.

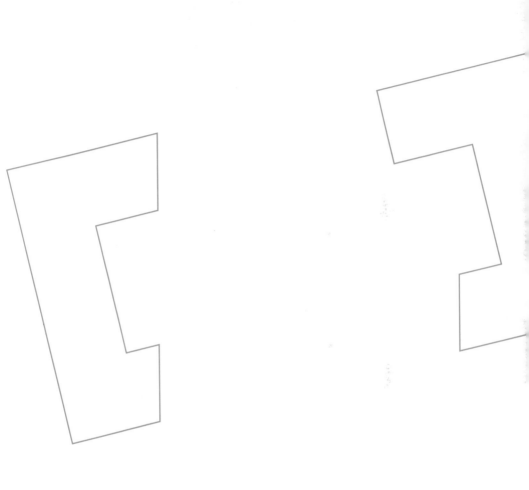

This space has been left for you.

STAGE SIX

KEEP GOING

"LEARN FROM YESTERDAY, LIVE FOR TODAY AND HOPE FOR TOMORROW."
ALBERT EINSTEIN*

*ALBERT EINSTEIN WAS A NOBEL PRIZE-WINNING PHYSICIST.

...AND THEN MY FOOT CAME OUT FROM UNDER ME AND I FELL HEAD FIRST INTO A COWPAT.
URGH! THAT'S SO GROSS.
I'M ***NEVER*** GOING TO A FARM IF THINGS LIKE THAT HAPPEN!
SLUMP
PAT PAT
FAIRLY CERTAIN THINGS LIKE THAT ONLY HAPPEN TO TJ.
WELCOME BACK! HOW ARE YOU ALL GETTING ON?

WELL GOOD, MAN.
YEAH, HAPPY.
I FEEL LIKE A WEIGHT'S BEEN LIFTED OFF ME.

THAT'S GREAT TO HEAR!
IT'S WONDERFUL TO SEE YOU ALL LOOKING SO POSITIVE AND OPTIMISTIC.
IT'S IMPORTANT TO KEEP THAT HEALTHY MINDSET IN LIFE.

CAN'T GET TAKEN IN BY THE ***DARK SIDE.***

EXPECT SETBACKS ALONG THE WAY

TICKLE
TICKLE
SSSSSS
SSSSSSS

IT MAY BE DIFFICULT AT TIMES, FEELING BOTH UPS AND DOWNS AS YOU GO.

JUST REMEMBER TO STAY FLEXIBLE AND KEEP ADJUSTING AS YOU GO.

WHAT IF WE GET SET BACK? OR IF WE FAIL?

FAILURE CAN BE HARD TO DEAL WITH. WE JUST HAVE TO REMEMBER TO BE KIND TO OURSELVES.

THERE WILL ALWAYS BE A NEW WAY TOWARDS YOUR DREAM.

FEEL YOUR GUT INSTINCT

BE DETERMINED AND DO YOUR BEST

"A DREAM DOESN'T BECOME REALITY THROUGH MAGIC. IT TAKES SWEAT, DETERMINATION AND HARD WORK."

THIS IS A QUOTE FROM COLIN POWELL, ONE OF THE MOST RESPECTED AMERICAN GENERALS OF HIS GENERATION.

THIS GUY WAS THE FIRST BLACK SECRETARY OF STATE.

TELL ME WHAT HIS QUOTE MAKES YOU THINK.

IT'S ABOUT DOING YOUR BEST.
YES. AND WHAT IS DOING YOUR BEST?
BEING DETERMINED. PUSHING YOURSELF.

IT'S ABOUT AIMING HIGH, BEING AMBITIOUS...
...BUT ALLOWING YOURSELF TO TAKE THE STEPS YOU NEED TO GET THERE.

AS PAUL ARDEN SAYS, "IT'S NOT HOW GOOD YOU ARE, IT'S HOW GOOD YOU WANT TO BE."

WORK HARD

COMMIT TO WHAT YOU'RE DOING

WORK SMART

BE CURIOUS, BE CREATIVE

BE CURIOUS

EVEN IF IT FEELS DIFFICULT

THERE ARE SOME OTHER THINGS THAT WILL HELP YOU STAY YOUR COURSE. BE CURIOUS AND STAY CURIOUS. WHAT DO YOU THINK THIS MEANS?
FINDING OUT HOW THINGS WORK AND WHY. ASKING PEOPLE UNTIL YOU UNDERSTAND?
YEAH, NO ONE'S GOING TO TEACH YOU. IT'S UP TO US TO MAKE SURE WE LEARN.
REMEMBER NOT TO LIMIT YOUR CURIOSITY AND KEEP ASKING QUESTIONS.

"WE SHOULDN'T WORRY WHEN WE FEEL OUT OF OUR DEPTH. THERE'S NO SUCH THING AS A STUPID QUESTION.

"YOU'LL BE SURPRISED HOW YOU'LL SET YOURSELF APART BY BEING BRAVE. FINDING THINGS OUT FOR YOURSELF IS ONE STEP FORWARD INTO A NEW ADVENTURE."
YEAH! WHO CARES WHAT OTHER PEOPLE THINK?!

*** AS ALICE IN WONDERLAND SAID: "CURIOUSER AND CURIOUSER..."**

SEEK OUT

MENTORS AND SUPPORTERS

THIS SPACE IS FOR YOUR REFLECTIONS | DATE: ....

WHO MIGHT BE A GOOD MENTOR FOR YOU?

Who do you know in your life that has the right qualities to be a good mentor for you? Where could you potentially seek one out?

WHY NOT EXPLORE?

KEEP GOING!

AS YOU PROGRESS, IT'S GOOD TO REFLECT ON WHAT YOU'VE ACHIEVED, NO MATTER HOW SMALL.

ESPECIALLY IF IT'S SOMETHING WE DON'T LIKE OR DIDN'T WANT TO DO.
YOU CAN LEARN MORE ABOUT YOURSELF AND HOW TO DO BETTER.

HOW DO YOU FEEL ABOUT KEEPING GOING? I WANT YOU TO WRITE DOWN WHAT'S IMPORTANT FOR YOU.
DO YOU FEEL YOU'RE ON THE RIGHT PATH NOW? WHAT MIGHT YOU NEED TO CHANGE?
TAKE TIME TO REFLECT. IT'S IMPORTANT TO FIND A QUIET TIME SO YOU CAN CHECK IN WITH YOURSELF.
WHEN AND WHERE COULD YOU DO THIS?

WRITE DOWN IN THREE COLUMNS: A) WHAT YOU'VE ACHIEVED, B) HOW YOU FELT, AND C) WHAT WAS DIFFICULT.
NEXT, WRITE DOWN WHAT YOU HAVE LEARNT ABOUT YOURSELF SO FAR. HAS ANYTHING SURPRISED YOU?
THINK ABOUT HOW YOU CAN BE HEALTHY AND WELL. REWARD YOURSELF. IT'S IMPORTANT THAT YOU CELEBRATE YOUR VICTORIES AND SUCCESSES.
[RE] START

THIS SPACE IS FOR YOUR REFLECTIONS | DATE: ....

WHAT HAVE YOU ACHIEVED SO FAR?

It's important to remember your achievements and successes so far. Each building block and step you take is bringing you closer to your dream.

THIS SPACE IS FOR YOUR REFLECTIONS | DATE: ....

HOW DO YOU FEEL?

Take time to think about your feelings. What have you found difficult? What have you enjoyed?

THIS SPACE IS FOR YOUR REFLECTIONS | DATE: ....

WHAT HAVE YOU LEARNT ABOUT YOURSELF SO FAR?

Did you try anything new?

THIS SPACE IS FOR YOUR REFLECTIONS / DATE: ....

HOW CAN YOU KEEP YOURSELF HEALTHY AND MINDFUL?

Give yourself quiet times to reflect and focus.

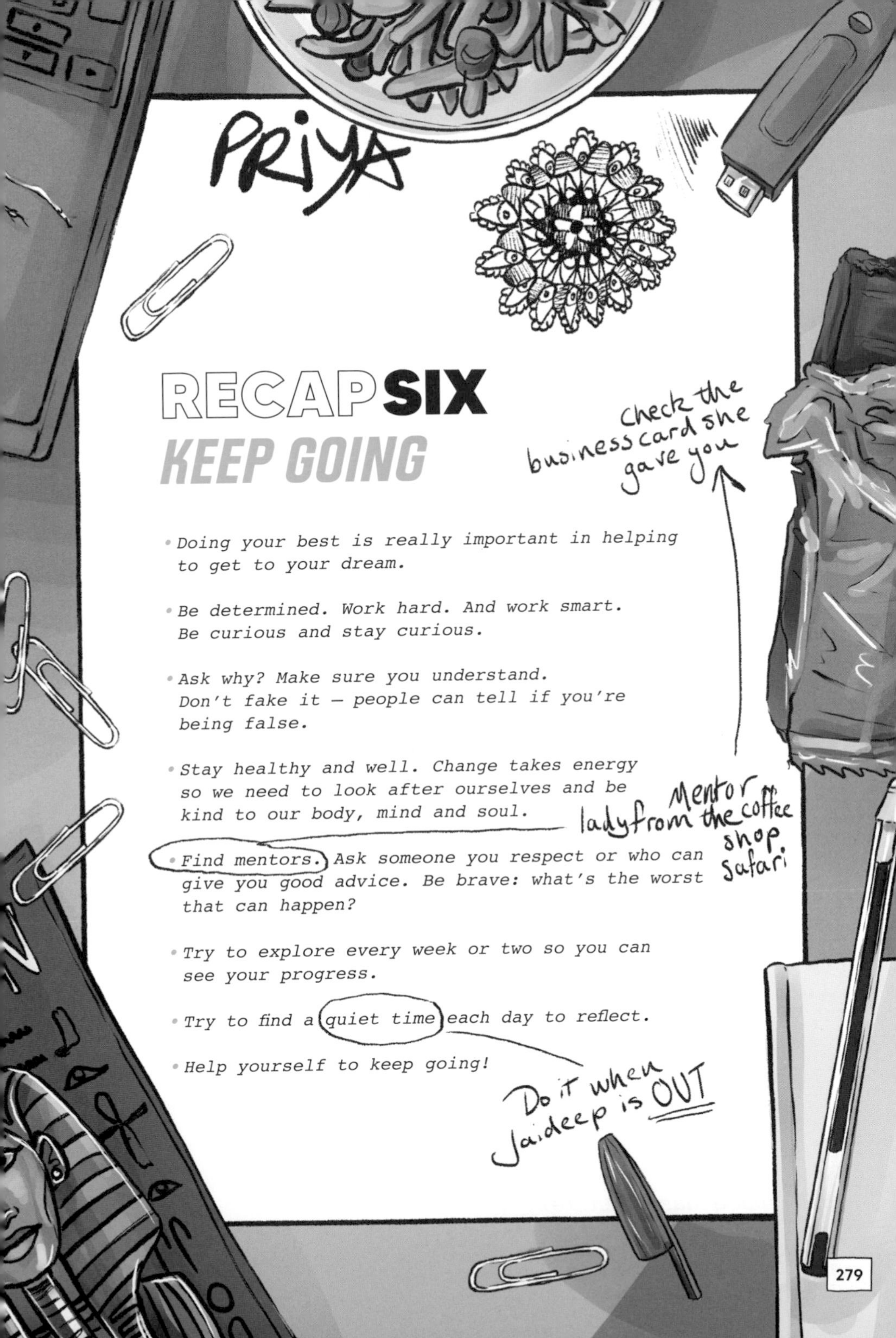

RECAP SIX
KEEP GOING

- Doing your best is really important in helping to get to your dream.
- Be determined. Work hard. And work smart. Be curious and stay curious.
- Ask why? Make sure you understand. Don't fake it – people can tell if you're being false.
- Stay healthy and well. Change takes energy so we need to look after ourselves and be kind to our body, mind and soul.
- Find mentors. Ask someone you respect or who can give you good advice. Be brave: what's the worst that can happen?
- Try to explore every week or two so you can see your progress.
- Try to find a quiet time each day to reflect.
- Help yourself to keep going!

PRiYA
Check the business card she gave you
Mentor
lady from the coffee shop
Safari
Do it when Jaideep is OUT

This space has been left for you.

EPILOGUE

REMEMBER: IT'S NEVER TOO LATE

I STILL CAN'T BELIEVE YOU JUST DELETED YOUR 'GRAM.
I KNOW, I'M ONE VERY PROUD MOTHER HEN!

I DO MISS IT. AND IT WASN'T A CURE. I STILL STRUGGLE.

BUT I KNOW I'LL HAVE MORE HELP SOON. ME AND MY MOMS HAVE FOUND A GOOD THERAPIST.

AWH, COME HERE, YOU!

THE GREEN SOC
ICELAND TRIP
April 16-26th
Information to sign up on the back of this leaflet.

IT'S FUNNY...

ERSTANDING YOUR GENDER
LOVE YOU BOTH. BYE!*
*TRANSLATED FROM CANTONESE.

STUDY ABROAD BUCKET LIST.

- Go to Comedy nights. ✓
- Find my "people." ✓
- Get involved in Communities. ✓
- Improve english. ✓
- Improve confidence! ✓

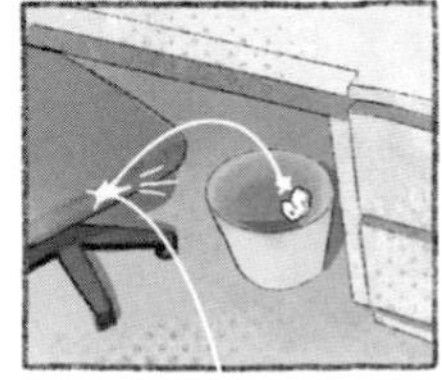

...DEPENDING ON THE SCHOOLS, YOUR MOTHER AND I CAN TAKE YOU TO INTERVIEWS...
...THOUGH I SUPPOSE YOU'LL NEED A PORTFOLIO.
PUTTING THAT TOGETHER WILL TAKE SOME TIME, AND WE ONLY HAVE UNTIL EACH DEAD-LINE TO DO THAT. DO YOU THINK THEY'LL ACCEPT YOU WITHOUT ONE OR...*
*TRANSLATED FROM PASHTO.
MY TEACHER TOLD ME THIS WAS A GREAT SCHOOL!
IT'S IN SCOTLAND, MASHOOMA.
AH... MOR. WOULD I NOT BE ALLOWED TO GO?
IT'S OK, I'LL TELL HIM. YOU KNOW, YOUR BABA HAS ALWAYS WANTED TO WEAR A KILT.

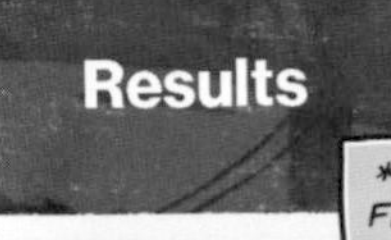
Results
NO WAY!*
*TRANSLATED FROM PUNJABI.
Dear Priya!
Congratulations, you are the winne
Thank you so much for applying t

LOOK!
LOOK!
I DID IT!
I WON THE COMPETITION TO NEW YORK!

WELL DONE, MY PUTTAR!

Smooth escape, be there in 20 xxx

pls say we're getting salted popcorn, or I'm turning around now... 😉

You're lucky I'm diabetic, or I'd be fighting...

Dw, it's on me, see you soon 😘

YOU'RE ON TIME?
WE DIDN'T BELIEVE IT, SO THE OTHERS ARE QUEUEING.

19:25
NEW MESSAGE

HOLD

ey Sophie?!

You coming out tonight or what? We haven't seen you in forever...

...

SWIPE

HA HA HA
HA HA HA

WHAT ARE YOU DOING! CLEARLY THAT'S THE WRONG WAY!
SHUT UP AND JUST WATCH THE MASTER AT WORK.
FAM YOU NEED STRONGER GLASSES, COS THIS IS EMBARRASSING.
UNKNOWN
I KNEW YOU'D GET THE GIG, BUD!
ONLY WITH YOUR HELP, MAN. SERIOUSLY, THANK YOU...
YEAH, MAN. NO SWEAT.
YOU CAN EXPECT MY INVOICE SOON.
ALARM
WHAT'S THAT FOR?
TRYING TO GET ON TOP OF MY TIME MANAGEMENT, INNIT.
LOOK AT YOU BEING ALL PROACTIVE.
YEAH, YEAH. I KNOW.
YOU KNOW I'M--
"MORE THAN JUST A PRETTY FACE!"
GEE, YOU THINK?
I'M BLUSHING.
ANYWAYS, CATCH YA LATER, STEVE JOBS. I GOTTA RUN!

AMERICANO, T.J.?

THANKS!

SINCE WHEN DO YOU DRINK COFFEE?
SINCE I LEARNED TO GROW UP.

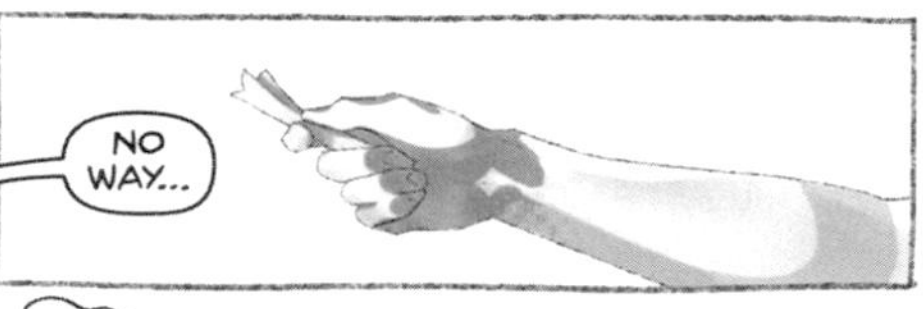
NO WAY...

YOU GOT ABDUCTED BY ALIENS. IT'S THE ONLY EXPLAN-ATION.

I SAID I'D PAY YOU BACK, AND WELL... SORRY IT'S LATE.

SLURP
BETTER LATE THAN NEVER.

YOU READY FOR THIS?
ABSOLUTELY NOT... BUT I STILL WANNA DO IT.

THANKS, G.

YOU GOT THIS, TEEJ.

HI THERE...
...YEAH, I'D LIKE TO BOOK IN FOR A SURGERY APPOINTMENT PLEASE...

THIS SPACE IS FOR YOUR REFLECTIONS | DATE: ....

HOW DO YOU FEEL NOW?

Write down how you feel about your journey. Is this different from when you started?

This space has been left for you.

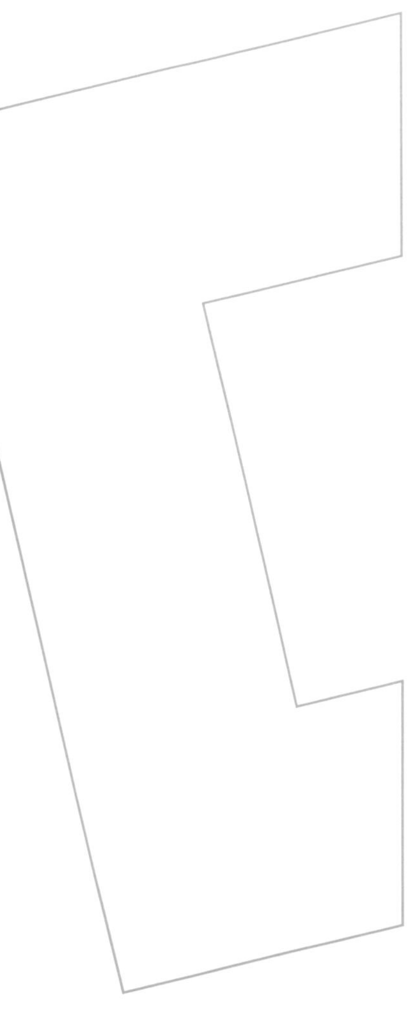

This space has been left for you.

This space has been left for you.

FOUNDER'S NOTE

I believe that everyone should have the opportunity to improve their situation and reach their potential. I also believe that everyone has different starting points, strengths and requirements to help them on their way.

This project was conceived to help people feel better about their current situation and what their future could be. The concept was largely inspired by my friendships over the years and experiences working at Reluctantly Brave, where I trained over 170 16-24-year-olds to consult with senior business leaders at world-class brands such as Nando's, Starbucks and Thomson Reuters. I co-founded this pioneering business with Dawood Gustave and my brother Jonathan in 2012, with compassion and inclusivity at its core.

It was obvious to me that given the right tools, anyone can achieve more than they imagine possible. Yet, so much business know-how and education isn't accessible. This led me to conceptualise this project before the pandemic.

It's been co-written by three young creatives: Julia Cockerham, Latreya Nelson and Eddy Nicholls. Our design team grew with illustrators Alex Copeman and Yabaewah Scott joining as well as a wider team of designers, editors, students and creatives. Over three years in the making, more than 50 people have been directly involved in creating this project (acknowledged on the right).

Leading this project has used all my skills (and more!). It's an ambitious undertaking in so many ways - more than I realised at the beginning. I'm thankful for my team and proud of how they've grown during the process. I'm also grateful for the support of my family, friends and colleagues.

Thank you all for helping to make this happen.

James Pattinson

OUR TEAM

Founder
James Pattinson

Co-writers
Julia Cockerham, Latreya Nelson, Eddy Nicholls

Illustrators
Julia Cockerham (Stage 2 and 6), Alex Copeman (Cover art, Stage 5 and Epilogue), Eddy Nicholls (Stage 1 and 3), Yabaewah Scott (Stage 4)

Lettering
HdE

Editors
Kirsten Murray, Neetu Singh

Advisors
Dawood Gustave, Dotti Irving, Tony Orsten, Anna Afolayan, Kirat Gata-Aura, Kevin Roberts, Joao Dias, Eliana Dias, Alex Grouet

Graphic design
Elen Swetman, Megan Freeman, Mathieu Cadelo

Translations
Shala Nyx, Neetu Singh, Hanqi Shen

Research and marketing
Elly Bonney, Amy McGrath, George Doel, Lucienne Labep, Joshua Okeyre, Latreya Nelson, Dean de Barros

PR
Dotti Irving, Neetu Singh, Eddy Nicholls, Rebecca Gray

Film
Barney Lankester-Owen, Deniz Oznacar, Katie Kingsman from Flow Films

Publishing
Amelia Collins, John Bond, Chris Wold, Jess King, Becky Miles, Julia Koppitz at Whitefox

Script reviewers
Tony Orsten, Aminata Sesay, Chevelle Orr, Emmanuella Antiedu, India Kaur, Darasimi Ogunleye, Joshua Okeyre, Matthew Chan, George Doel, Lucie Labep, Amy McGrath, Mabel Lee, Hanqi Shen, Freddie Doel, Max Ramsden, Charlotte Lazarus, Harry Purvis

Other people who have helped us along the way
Bibby Keryn, Natalie Hayes, Erin Charles, Wendy Hodgkiss, David Bradshaw, Tom Morris, Samata Pattinson, Jonathan Pattinson, Adam Papaphilippopoulos, Tamara Stoll, Mike Fordham, Lord Chris Smith, Ed Elliott, Reluctantly Brave's (Young) Braves: Davidson Otobo, Kangana Parmar, Zainab Alshaba, Xaymaca Awoyungbo, Haris Kiani, David Ewhieberene, Ruhena Begum, Callum Taylor @libraryofcalcifer, Kemi Ayorinde & Busayo Matuluko @compulsivebookbuyers, Rosie Crawford @just_a_little_roo, Amy Andrawas @amymaybooks

Our parents and loved ones

ABOUT THE CREATORS

[Re]Start has been co-created by a team with diverse backgrounds and experiences, to provide authentic insights, points of view and storytelling. Our aim is to support and encourage our readers to believe in themselves, realise their passions and follow their dreams.

James Pattinson

James conceptualised *[Re]Start: It's Never Too Late* just before the COVID-19 pandemic. His work has long been founded on principles of access and inclusion; from mentoring young people while a Global Brand Manager at P&G to co-founding creative consultancy Reluctantly Brave, where he trained over 170 16-24-year-olds to consult for world-class brands. James is an award-winning strategist and entrepreneur and studied at the University of Oxford and, later, University of Cambridge. He currently lives in London.

Eddy Nicholls

Eddy is an illustrator and writer, and while working on *[Re]Start: It's Never Too Late* he fulfilled both these roles, as well as Creative Team Leader. A Falmouth University graduate, he was born in Bristol where he self-published his first graphic novel at the age of 14. Eddy has always been passionate about visual storytelling and firmly believes in its power to positively impact the world. Outside of illustration, he is a keen musician and outdoor enthusiast. He is now based in Manchester.

Julia Cockerham

Julia is a Cornish Illustrator and Falmouth University graduate. She is a co-writer and co-illustrator of *[Re]Start: It's Never Too Late.* She has been with the project since its inception. Since applying for this role through her university bulletin during the pandemic, she has since become a full-time illustrator with the ambition to author many more stories in the future. Julia is passionate about storytelling, books and musical theatre, and enjoys performing in productions across Cornwall.

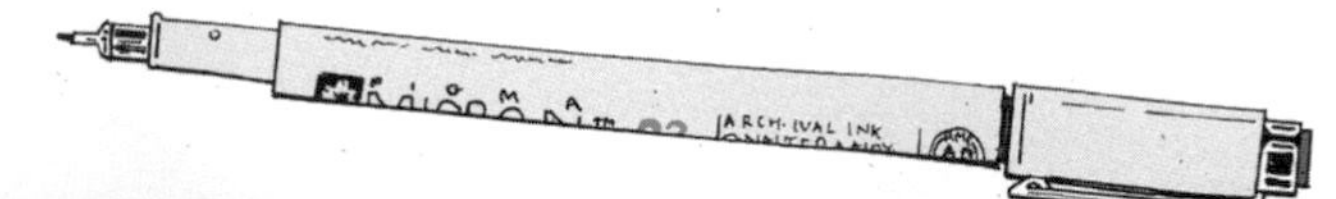

Latreya Nelson

Latreya is a Caribbean East Londoner and University of Arts London graduate. She is a co-writer and digital creative of *[Re]Start: It's Never Too Late.* Latreya completed her MA at UAL during the pandemic and, following her graduation, sourcing employment was bleak. However, she instantly felt deeply connected to [Re]Start and what it stands for. Whether it's creating her stories through illustration or animation, or reading books or films, Latreya yearns to share all stories with the world.

Yabaewah Scott

Yabaewah studied Graphic Design and Illustration at university. She is a co-illustrator on *[Re]Start: It's Never Too Late.* After seeing the early stages of the creative process and hearing [Re]Start's mission, she was inspired to be a part of the team. Within her work, Yabaewah enjoys a bold use of colour and texture and would describe herself as a curious creative with a love for animals. She currently works as a teacher.

Alex Copeman

Alex Copeman is an Illustrator from the North West and the final co-illustrator to join *[Re]Start: It's Never Too Late.* After graduating from the University of Falmouth during the pandemic, when all support systems collapsed, he committed to building an art social media platform that grew significantly. Through this, he has managed to build a portfolio of both commercial and personal work that strives for diversity and inclusivity, and is his main ambition when creating art.

RESOURCES

General support and advice

Citizens Advice Bureau: www.citizensadvice.org.uk
Childline: www.childline.org.uk

Anxiety, depression and mental health support

The Samaritans: www.samaritans.org
Mind: www.mind.org.uk
Young Minds: www.youngminds.org.uk

Advice on bullying

Ditch the abuse: www.ditchthelabel.org
Family lives: www.familylives.org.uk
Childline: www.childline.org.uk
NSPCC: www.nspcc.org.uk

Suppport on domestic violence

NHS helpline: www.gov.uk/guidance/domestic-abuse-how-to-get-help
Women's Aid: www.womensaid.org.uk/information-support
NSPCC: www.nspcc.org.uk
Refuge: www.nationaldahelpline.org.uk

Advice on living with a disability

Disability Rights: www.disabilityrightsuk.org

Advice on bereavement

Cruse: www.cruse.org.uk

Support on race and identity

Mind: www.mind.org.uk
Sari: www.saricharity.org.uk
The Community Security Trust (National Organisation for Jewish victims): www.cst.org.uk
Tell MAMA (National Organisation for Muslim victims): www.tellmamauk.org

Support on sexuality and sexual identity

Asexual Visibility and Education Network: www.asexualityarchive.com
Stonewall: www.stonewall.org.uk
LGBT Foundation: https://lgbt.foundation/
Pink Therapy resources: www.pinktherapy.com/en-gb/knowledge.aspx
Anyone and Everyone: www.anyoneandeveryone.com
It Gets Better Project: www.itgetsbetter.org
It Gets Better (video: Apple employees): https://www.youtube.com/watch?v=iWYqsaJk_U8
It Gets Better (video: Centre Theatre Group): https://www.youtube.com/watch?v=NOzUYVGKESQ

Advice on gender

Gendered Intelligence: http://genderedintelligence.co.uk/
Pink Therapy resources: http://www.pinktherapy.com/en-gb/knowledge.aspx
Jay's story (NHS video): https://www.youtube.com/watch?v=11dlo_tOrFY
Ruth's story (NHS video): https://www.youtube.com/watch?v=2SZdEoxty_Y